Kath &

C000002786

The Woman Who Didn't Exist

KATH & CLIVE RICHARDSON

RIVERHEAD

For further information about 'The Woman Who Didn't Exist'
visit our website at: thewomanwhodidntexist.com

A CIP catalogue record for this book is
available from the British Library

ISBN 978-0-9929225-0-4

Design and Production by Riverhead, Hull
44-46 High Street, Hull, East Yorkshire. HU1 1PS
Telephone: 01482 318218
email: mike@riverheadbooks.karoo.co.uk

Printed by: Fisk Printers, Hull

This book is dedicated to our four
very special and much loved grandchildren -
Katie, Jacob, Noah and Molly-Rose.

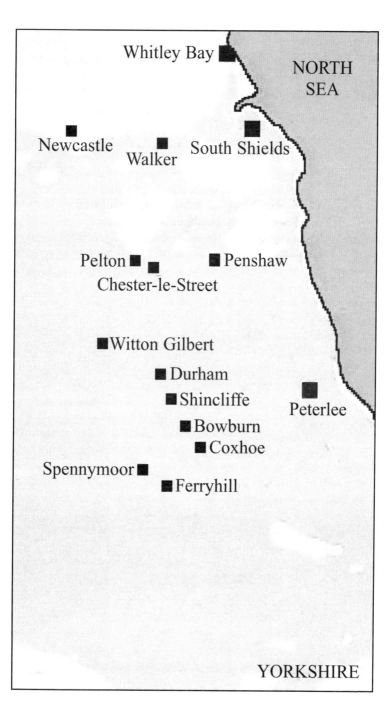

PROLOGUE

Victorian England was renowned for its high moral standpoint; people were generally God fearing and followed a strict code of conduct, based on Christian virtues.

Family life was important as it encouraged hard work and respectability. Father, as head of the household, was very strict and expected to be obeyed by everyone whilst a woman's role was that of a supportive wife. On marrying, she was forced to leave full time employment with child bearing becoming her main occupation.

It was an era of prudishness, when ladies were expected to dress and behave modestly ensuring their arms, legs and shoulders were covered at all times. Issues relating to sexual matters, such as contraception, were rarely discussed. Mothers who gave birth illegitimately were considered extremely sinful and were made to feel social outcasts. Women, in unhappy and sometimes violent marriages, were trapped, as divorce was not considered an option.

Yet if you scratched beneath the surface, it became apparent that not all women conformed to these strong social ethics. Prostitution was rife in the cities, back street abortionists were plying their trade and women were risking bigamous marriages to escape previous loveless unions.

Towards the end of the nineteenth century, however, attitudes were beginning to change. Women were demanding more from life than an endless cycle of pregnancy or a life spent in domestic service. They felt it unfair that men had so many more privileges and that they controlled the public sphere of society. Some women were seeking equal opportunities for themselves and there were even a group of feminists, demanding the right to vote!

They had no indication that an event was soon to happen which would indeed change their lives forever. World War One, spanning 1914 to 1918, was to be the first war ever, to affect an entire civilian population and by the end of it, many women had their first taste of social and financial independence. Their low self-images had faded and now they were ready to stand on their own two feet.

It was against this backdrop that Margaret Burns was born. She was no different from the masses. Born in 1889, into a mining community, in Cumberland, her future was destined to be as

5

ordinary and predictable as the majority of the working class women of her day. No one could have foreseen the way her life would become so extraordinary.

What follows is a true story, although, at times, that is difficult to believe. All the main characters, the dates and the places mentioned are genuine and the majority of events described actually took place. Unfortunately, more than half the service records, for the British Army in World War One, were destroyed in September 1940, when a German bombing raid struck the War Office repository in London. This included the records of Margaret Burns' husband, therefore it has been almost impossible to verify certain details of his war service, such as if and when he was granted leave during his years of fighting. So, a few assumptions have had to be made. Naturally, most of the conversations and feelings expressed are mere conjecture, although some have been recounted, almost word for word, by the descendants of Margaret Burns - 'The Woman who didn't exist.'

ONE
Bowburn, County Durham - 1917

'Stop 'em ma! Can't you stop 'em?' shouted Jacob in defiant mood. But his ma, Maggie Purvis, shook her head. Visibly shaking, she watched in silence, with a mixture of utter disbelief and a growing sense of injustice.

The three colliery officials continued their task of eviction, with such an apparent lack of feeling, that it totally overwhelmed her. Her worldly possessions might be few and not amount to much but nevertheless it was still heart breaking to see them stacked in a heap on the pavement. Worse still, was being forced from this rented, end of terrace miner's house, which had been her home for the last ten years and a happy one for the most part. Maggie could almost accept the men's disinterest in her but how could they be so cruel to her four bewildered children who were looking on?

Jacob, the oldest of the four, was so annoyed he persisted in kicking stones against the coalman's old wooden cart, acting as the removal vehicle, despite the presence of a policeman. His mother, so preoccupied, just ignored him. Little John-George, his youngest brother, failed to understand any significance to the ensuing events, as he was not yet two, but cowered against his mother's skirt. His seven year old sister Ann was equally bemused and remained silent whilst Roland, although only four, displayed a certain maturity beyond his years:

'What's to become of us, ma?' he demanded, 'where'll we go?'

'Shurrup!' snorted Jacob, as the latest stone ricocheted off the cart and caught the horse's fetlock, causing it to rear up.

With that, John-George began to cry and Maggie, in her frustration, whipped round and slapped Jacob full across the face. Jacob, red haired and with a matching attitude, pretended not to care but feelings of anger and resentment towards his mother were heightened by the shame he felt at his family's eviction. On this occasion, however, the force of the blow told him that he best keep quiet.

Maggie had never felt more in despair but was determined not to give the men the satisfaction of showing her outrage.

'Don't you worry now Roland, this ain't the end of us, come follow me,' she sneered loudly.

Then she spun round and rushed off down the narrow, cobbled street, with all four children, plus horse, cart and driver, trailing behind her. She marched on, quickening her pace, past the red bricked, two-up, two-down houses, each identical to the previous one.

This was Bowburn, a small mining village four miles south of Durham, with a growing population of over a thousand inhabitants. It had been created around a mine and its buildings and layout were typical of the area. There were just five back-to-back streets, three beer houses, a few shops and more recently a village school. The houses had no front gardens, just door after door, opening outwards onto narrow pavements.

Each house had its knocker up handle, to be used by the colliery officials, to ensure the miners were punctual for their shift. Every front door had its immaculate donkey stoned doorstep, which was being cleaned that very day, just as they were every Monday without fail.

But today Maggie ignored those who were busy at their ritual. Usually she would have stopped to make polite conversation but today was certainly not an occasion for idle chat, especially feeling as bitter as she did. She was sure someone in this street must have reported her. Who was her betrayer? Why hadn't they minded their own business? No wonder I'm so embittered, she thought to herself when I've been given this 'punishment', which my family and I certainly don't deserve.

Her despair seemed to escalate as she reached the outskirts of the village and began to realise the enormity of what was happening and its impact on her family. She headed for the large field, which bordered the main road. It was an unusually cool summer day, with air that was damp and somewhat chilly. Roland, a chronic asthmatic, found his breathing hampered as he struggled to keep pace with his mother, causing him to cough relentlessly. Maggie, with her thoughts definitely elsewhere, seemed unconcerned at his plight. She continuously urged the children to quicken their pace, as if their life depended on it, even though the truth was that there was nowhere to hurry to. The long grass in the field was wet underfoot but the children's footwear, hand-me-downs and more than once, was totally inadequate. She appeared completely oblivious to this too.

By now, Jacob had bounded ahead to the far end of the field, attracted by what he'd seen. For there in the meadow, were what Maggie hoped would be her source of salvation - a group of old army bell tents. There were about a hundred in total, all in close proximity. These tents had been erected the previous year, for use by older pitmen from down south. They had been recruited to replace the younger colliery men, who'd left the mines to enlist as war volunteers. Some tents had now been vacated and were merely empty shells, with the barest of essentials still inside. Maggie quickly assessed the situation and chose one in the middle of the group.

'This'll be the warmest one, I reckon,' she mused and Roland, who was the only one to show any concern, agreed.

Having made her decision, she said goodbye to the carter who kindly deposited her belongings outside her chosen tent. Maggie urged the children to go inside and apart from Jacob, they all complied. To Ann and John-George it seemed quite exciting - a bit of an adventure - and they ran around, throwing themselves on the rough canvas flooring. Roland helped his mother unpack their few meagre possessions from an old battered suitcase and several boxes. These included an old brass oil lamp, some well-worn blankets, a few items of essential clothing, the simplest of cooking equipment, plus a few groceries and toys. Poignantly, there, lying at the bottom of a box was Jacob's wooden toy cart, which his father had handcrafted so lovingly, soon after his birth, but which was now treasured by Roland.

There were several miners occupying a group of tents nearby and later that evening a couple of them, William and Robert, willingly acquainted Maggie with the general layout of the place, particularly where to access water from the pump and the rudimentary toilet facilities. They even invited Maggie to share a drink but on this occasion she declined,

'Thanks for the offer but it's been a long hard day and I've still to get the young 'uns to sleep,' she explained as she ushered the children back to the tent. She was glad she had an excuse, for in reality, being sociable was the last thing on her mind.

Sleep though was not on Jacob's agenda. Instead, he disappeared for a couple of hours. Although only eight and quite small in stature, he came across as confident and street wise. He had long been allowed to roam at will. His independence was accepted by Maggie, even encouraged. He had always seemed a troubled child but his behaviour had definitely deteriorated in recent months.

Maggie found his moods tiresome and argued with him frequently. Her attitude was 'out of sight, out of mind,' when he went off. She barely missed his presence except when she needed him to look after his younger siblings or do his share of the daily chores.

Finally he returned, but well after the dark night sky had

plunged them into total darkness. The pitch black frightened John-George and he clung to his big sister for comfort. Roland was more resilient, despite his worsening health.

'Don't you be crying our John-George, there's no good it'll do you. We're here now and our ma will look after us,' he reassured his younger brother.

'I want summat to eat,' piped up Ann but there was nothing to be had and so that was the end of the matter.

That night they all went to bed hungry but somehow, eventually, they managed to sleep fairly soundly but only for a while. The cold night air chilled them and they became restless, missing the comfort of their beds. Maggie was first awake, around dusk and as she lay on the hard floor, she pondered her fate. How had things come to this? She could feel one of her black moods descending. All too familiar with hardship and suffering, for a moment she gave way to self-pity but it was set aside for a while when she became aware of the familiar signs that her family were stirring.

Maggie, always one to encourage independence, expected the children to both dress and feed themselves. But with the children wearing the clothes they went to bed in and, having little in the way of food, this was not an option. Maggie actually felt quite concerned, even guilty, and repeatedly promised her aggrieved children that this situation would soon be rectified. She was all too aware her main priority, now that she had some basic shelter at least, was to support her family financially. Certainly she knew the mining company wouldn't be supporting her any longer.

No money ultimately meant starvation but earning a living was a huge problem when you were virtually unemployable, due to present circumstances. She fully accepted that she must use whatever means she could to find an income. In fact she'd only survived in recent months by obtaining money in ways she considered quite shameful. Maybe it was that behaviour, she concluded, which had led to her present predicament though she still wasn't certain of either the reason or the person, responsible for her eviction.

Maggie had constantly tried to be a strong, resourceful woman, with a gritty determination to accept – even enjoy-whatever life threw at her. However, recent events had so affected her spirits, she realised that she would struggle to cope with this seemingly intolerable situation. The negative thoughts she had experienced earlier kept careering around her head, creating a great cloud of despondency that seemed to completely overwhelm her. Her greatest fear - having to go into the workhouse - seemed to be a distinct possibility at this moment in time. Why did life give her such a raw deal? What had she ever done, that was so wicked that she deserved to be punished in this way? Hadn't she had more than enough to cope with in the past, without this present predicament… and all before her thirtieth birthday?

TWO
28 years earlier... Whitehaven, Cumberland - 1889

Margaret Burns - the future Maggie Purvis - was born in 1889, on a Sunday. It was the middle of June, with warm and pleasant weather outside but inside, confined in the small bedroom of a miner's cottage, in Keekle Terrace, Hensingham, the heat was stifling.

'It's a girl and it looks like she's going to be a redhead!' announced the local midwife who was dripping with sweat and feeling a great surge of relief that she had enabled Mary to deliver her sixth baby safely.

'Would you like me to go and tell your husband?' she continued, as she moved towards the stairs.

'Go on then,' replied an exhausted Mary, 'better let him know he has a third daughter.'

'Shall we call her Margaret, after my grandmother?' Mary suggested to Jacob a few days later, not that her husband was especially bothered about the choice of name. Nor was he particularly excited about the arrival of this latest child. To him, the birth of Margaret meant yet another mouth to feed, as well as providing for his existing family of five, the oldest of whom was ten-year-old Nancy. There was little doubting Jacob loved his children but providing for their needs was a constant, on-going problem. Mary harboured similar reservations about this new baby but for an entirely different reason.

She really hoped Margaret would be her last child as she was growing weary of the endless cycle of pregnancy and childbirth. Realistically though, she knew this child was unlikely to be her final one.

'Unpleasant things will happen to you when you get married but learn to put up with it,' her mother had warned her, prior to her marriage to Jacob Burns in 1877, at the local register office in Whitehaven.

Put up with 'it' she did but the question of birth control was foremost in Mary's mind, even though Jacob rarely referred to it. There were few options available anyway but it didn't curtail Mary's desire to ensure that no further babies were conceived.

She secretly hoped that breast-feeding her baby would act as a deterrent, for a while at least and provide a 'safe' period. It was either that or abstention but she knew Jacob wouldn't be happy to be denied, what he considered to be his marital rights, for very long. He was quite demanding and she knew ultimately there was no guaranteed way of avoiding the inevitable.

Her husband was of Irish descent, typically hot headed and passionate, with a great wit and ability to charm. Although generally kind, he had a quick temper when roused. He'd never raised his hand to Mary but she knew there was an unwritten rule to always comply with his wishes.

The children also learned not to cross him when he was in one of 'his moods', knowing that his belt would be quickly removed and used to good effect. Not that the children saw a lot of their da as he worked an eight-hour shift, six days every week. Even on the days when he felt unwell, he had to force himself to go down the mine, as the fear of debt was never far away.

Just like his own father before him, Jacob was employed as a coal hewer, at the local pit. The job demanded a strong constitution for it meant working underground in a four-foot high tunnel, stacking up the roof of the coal seam with pit props and then hewing away at the coalface. The work was dangerous with many potential hazards including explosions, fires, flooding and roof collapses. It was also a physically demanding job. Jacob found it back breaking and he knew that the damp and dusty conditions, especially in such a confined space were detrimental to his health. His persistent cough worried him, convinced that he was developing permanent lung disease, like so many of his fellow pit men. Even his hearing was affected by the constant noise of dripping water. Mary found she had to raise her voice to him, just to make herself heard.

'Here's your bait,' she would say to him every morning as she passed him his jam sandwiches, along with his bottle of cold tea and his tabs that he rolled himself.

'I'm not late!' he would sometimes snap back but Mary would simply smile to herself.

'I'll see you tonight,' would always be his last words as he walked out the door and he'd turn and look at his wife with a knowing smile.

Mary knew exactly what he meant. On his return, he always expected his tea to be on the table, followed by his warm bath in front of the fire, with a change of clothes ready waiting for him. Then, for the rest of the evening, he would go down the road to 'The Keekle Inn' always justifying it with the same excuse,

'It's dusty work down the shaft, I need me liquid refreshment to clear me lungs.'

He'd return a couple of hours later, in various states of intoxication. Mary was grateful for the nights when he simply fell into bed and instantly went to asleep. More often than not, he pestered her, wanting to have his way with her. Sometimes she lied and told him she was having her women's troubles or pretended to be fast asleep but more often than not, he succeeded in his quest. Mary fretted constantly that their union would produce another child and was always comforted when her monthlies arrived on time.

She was constantly worried about the amount of money her husband spent on drink but felt she had to hold her counsel. At the end of each week, he brought home almost twenty shillings which was never enough as far as she was concerned. Making ends meet was a permanent struggle. For as well as providing food and clothes for all the family, some of Jacob's wages had to be put aside for his work needs. Every pitman was expected to purchase his own work tools from the local store. The price of a pickaxe alone was four shillings, meaning certain luxuries, such as a lamp, were out of the question.

'Better to buy twelve candles for one penny,' Jacob explained to his sons, knowing they would one day follow him into the mine, ' than one of those carbide lamps for six shillings!'

'I'm in need of some new pads,' Mary would hear him complain nearly every month. Using them to strap around his knees for protection, as he crawled along the rough, uneven floor of the tunnels, meant they were quickly worn through and needed replacing.

'Not this week,' Mary would insist, 'the girls are in need of some new boots,' or she would cite something similar. Jacob accepted that he'd have to make do with his old ones for yet a bit longer.

The one plus side to being a miner was the small terraced house that was available to rent from his employers. His present home, in Keekle Terrace, stood in a long, single row of around thirty dwellings, lining the main road, with no other houses either behind or opposite. Instead they overlooked the railway line but beyond were the majestic hills of the Lake District and an immense swathe of green pastureland. Mary though had little appreciation for the location with its impressive view. Her concerns were directed at the restricting size of the property, for being just two-up, two-down, there was limited room for their growing family.

'Go outside and play!' Mary ordered the children most mornings and even the youngest child would soon be toddling onto the street, along with the rest of them, to play in the field beyond.

14

'We shall have to move,' Mary suggested to her husband, as he returned from his shift one evening. It had poured with rain all day, confining the children indoors and had simply confirmed to Mary what she already knew:

'This house just ain't big enough for the eight of us,' she continued in exasperation.

What Jacob didn't realise, was that Mary was feeling very despondent for another reason. For in the winter of 1889, she realised that the inevitable had happened. She was expecting her seventh child.

'I'm in the family way again,' she sighed loudly, hoping this news might add weight to her desire to move. Jacob could sense her frustration:

'I'll look for new employment,' he ventured, 'I think the coal seam I'm working on is just about empty so I could soon be moved on anyway.'

'The sooner, the better,' Mary muttered and really hoped they weren't empty promises that he was making.

Several weeks later, the whole family found themselves at the railway station, carrying the minimum of possessions, ready to journey the full width of the country to the north east of England. Jacob had secured employment down a mine near Newcastle where he'd been informed, by a 'scout' from that area, that the pay and conditions were slightly better.

The children were delighted by the prospect of their first train journey. They'd never been further than the main town of Whitehaven, just a mile up the road and they saw it as a wonderful adventure. The older ones clambered into a large carriage, each one of them eager to claim the outside seat so that they could press their noses against the window. Mary and Jacob followed, with Margaret, not yet one, scooped up in her father's arms. Not aware of what was happening, she soon fell asleep on Jacob's shoulder whilst her brothers and sisters gave a running commentary about the sights and sounds of the countryside. They were especially excited to see the steam rising from the engine's chimney, each time the carriages veered round yet another curve of the track.

It was, however, a long journey of over a hundred miles, travelling in third class accommodation and by the time they finally reached their destination, everyone was tired and hungry and their initial enthusiasm had worn thin. Mary, particularly, wasn't feeling too well and was singularly unimpressed by what she saw as they entered the pit village near South Shields.

A huge engine house and its wheels dominated the skyline. There were endless rows of back to back terraced houses, with their bleak exteriors of grimy red bricks. Why it's worse than the place we've left, was her immediate reaction and she now began to realise how fortunate she'd been to have a stunning countryside view, back in Keekle Terrace. But best keep such thoughts to me 'sen, she decided. Jacob won't appreciate criticism and there's no point in complaining - it certainly won't get me anywhere.

A small crowd of children gathered as they stood outside, surveying their new home. Mary entered first and immediately felt the dampness of the empty rooms.

'Best get a fire going,' she suggested to Jacob, 'and I'll make up the beds.'

The children ran excitedly into the cement yard, adjoining the back of the house but quickly decided it would be much more fun to go out front and explore their surroundings.

'Don't be staying out 'til after dark!' Mary ordered, 'I expect you to be back at teatime. And Nancy, I need you to go to the local store and buy me some provisions.'

Gradually, Mary settled into routine and made the acquaintance of other mothers in the street. The four oldest children adapted into their new school, whilst Hannah, at three, was old enough to amuse herself. Even Margaret was weaned and beginning to sleep through the night. But within months, Mary gave birth to a fourth daughter whom she named Catherine and once again she felt the heavy weight of motherhood bearing down on her.

Bringing up seven children was a daunting task but made even more difficult by the approaching winter when even menial chores required extra effort. There was no heating to keep the family warm, apart from the coal fire in the living room and that needed making on a daily basis.

'William, I'm putting you in charge of making up the fire every morning and cleaning it out at night,' Mary ordered her nine-year-old son. He was happy to comply, being the oldest boy, he regarded himself as 'the man of the house' when his da was at work.

The monotonous round of laundry was a constant issue, as the lack of adequate washing facilities made it really hard work. There was a poss tub in the outhouse, which first needed filling with heated water. The water had to be fetched from the outside tap.

'Owen, it's your job to fill the bucket with water, before you go to school, and bring it to me to put in the boiler at the side of the open fire,' Mary ordered her seven year old son.

Owen didn't complain but sometimes he found the temperature outside had plummeted in the night and the water in the tap had frozen.

'Drat the tap!' he grumbled one morning as his father was just setting out for his shift.

'Lost yer cap!' his da repeated, 'you better find it son, cos you'll not be getting another one.'

Owen decided to stay silent, knowing his da wouldn't appreciate being teased about his deafness. Besides, he was more concerned about his mother's reaction when she found out there was no water available. He knew his da's mining clothes would need seeing to, in time for the next day's shift and they alone created endless work for his mother. It was a real head ache to remove the dust then scrub, wash and dry them in time, especially as the damp winter air meant there was no point in trying to dry them outside. Instead, they had to be hung up inside, on the wooden rack, above the open fire grate in the kitchen.

'Mind that fire!' was Mary's constant refrain to the youngest children. She lived in fear of them getting too close, as they pushed past the rows of dangling clothes. She was all too aware of the dangers. She hadn't forgotten a young child back in Whitehaven whose flannel nightdress had caught alight in just this way and suffered horrific burns.

When it was time to iron the clothes, she was equally vigilant, insisting,

'Nancy you can help me with the ironing but you must always let me put the flat iron on the embers to be heated.'

Nancy, as the oldest girl, was expected to help her mother with most of the daily household chores. But on baking day, which was every Saturday, even the two youngest girls were encouraged to watch as their mother magically transformed her ingredients of diced meat, flour, lard and water into something edible - usually a pot pie, using the cheapest cuts of meat she could find. She would make and roll out the pastry on the large wooden table.

'You can brush the pie with a spot of milk,' she'd say to one of them, 'it'll give it a good old shine.'

Then she'd place it in the oven, at the side of the huge iron range and they'd all wait patiently for it to be removed to see the end result.

When Mary discovered she was running out of one of the basics, she'd tell Nancy to go to the local store,

'Just go to the Co-op and fetch me some sugar, Nancy, and take Margaret and Hannah with you,' she'd usually say, hoping to have a few minutes alone with the baby. Margaret loved walking alongside her big sister, holding her hand, or better still, if it were icy, she'd slide in the tracks left by the wooden cartwheels. Going into the shop was an even better treat. It was a fascinating place with its vast range of goods and even though she wasn't allowed to ever buy any-thing, it provided wonderful sights, sounds and smells. There was a complete assortment of goods, not just groceries but shoes, hardware, drapery and even hats of every kind. The elderly shopkeeper was a kindly, jolly man and he had a soft spot for Margaret. He would always remark on her beautiful auburn hair and sometimes even allowed her to try on a hat or two. Occasionally, he would press a boiled sweet into her hand, which to Margaret was an unimaginable treat.

'I'll get the divvy next week, as another three months has passed,' Mary would sometimes tell them on their return, 'so I'll perhaps be able to afford to buy you some fruit or maybe a few sweets, next time.'

But they grew to accept this as an empty promise, as there was always some more essential item that was needed, when the dividend was finally collected.

Mary's other concern was the constant need to provide clothes for her growing children and with little in the way of heating in their home, she was aware they should be warm ones. The younger children were used to wearing 'hand me downs' and Mary would patch them when they showed signs of wear but they were never adequate to keep out the cold.

'You can help me darn these socks, Nancy - you need to learn for when you have bairns of your own,' Mary demanded but she recognised that it was often a pointless task as they were too far gone.

Sometimes when the clothes became too old and threadbare to recycle, Mary would offer them to the ragman. Margaret especially loved it when she heard his horse and cart clip- clopping up the street.

'Rag and bone! Rag and bone!' the man cried and his booming voice would echo down the entire street, announcing his imminent arrival. The children all loved to mimic him, and if they were outside at the time, they would rush over to pat the old Shire horse. Mother would show him her offerings, hoping for a copper or two but usually the man was reluctant to give her anything for them.

'He's a mean old devil that he is, why he's not given me so much as a penny today!' Mary would grumble after he'd gone. 'Right, these will just have to be used to make another proddy mat.'

Margaret would watch as her mother and the older children tore up the threadbare clothes into long strips. All the family would then sit around the table, helping, with different degrees of success,

18

to weave these lengths into a piece of hessian, using a mat prodder.

Margaret was quite spellbound as a pattern gradually emerged with a black border and a mixed coloured centre. Mary was happy too as it meant all her children were occupied and under her watchful eye.

Mary prided herself on keeping her house spotless. On a different day, each week, she performed her rituals: black leading the stove, white washing the hearth, polishing the fender, cleaning the windows and scrubbing the front doorstep. But all these daily routines meant Mary worked seven days a week, all the year round.

The strain of looking after her growing family was starting to take its toll on both Mary's youthful looks and her general health. Despite only being in her mid-thirties, her face was that of a much older woman and her body appeared undernourished and weak. When money was tight, the last person to eat was always herself.

'Why there's nothing on yer lass, you're wasting away,' Jacob would complain but he never lifted a finger to help her with the endless chores. She was frequently exhausted and had begun to suffer from severe stomach cramps. She knew her health was suffering but what choice did she have? Doctors were expensive and there was no one to call on to alleviate her workload. What choice did any woman have unless you were 'a lady' and could afford a maid? There was no escaping the endless cycle of work and motherhood.

What particularly frustrated Mary was how unsettled Jacob was in his employment. Within the year of their arrival in the area he declared that he'd found work at a pit further north in Bedlington. So in late 1891, the family found themselves on the move again.

'253 Yard Row!' Mary looked at the address and sighed, 'it sounds like it's identical to where we've come from - a row of houses with simple backyards!'

'The pay's better though,' Jacob argued, 'it's worth a move, Mary.'

Mary tolerated it, as always, and was heartened when she saw the village consisted of just one wide street about a mile in length, not too dissimilar to her home back in Cumberland. But what she hadn't bargained for, was within months of the move, she discovered that she was expecting for the eighth time. She was in total despair at the prospect of giving birth again, so soon after Catherine, plus coping with the needs of a further child. Despite Jacob's wage increase, the purchase of extra nutritious food during her pregnancy was never considered her entitlement. There was no way either that she could take life any easier. In fact it was just

19

expected that she would continue with the never ending round of daily chores, right up to the day of delivery.

Worse still, as the day of her confinement drew close, yet again Jacob decided to move. He announced that they were to go back south to the village of Walker where some of their family lived and he'd secured a miner's house in Cambrian Row. He thought the fact that his cousin lived there was an advantage but Mary wasn't at all impressed. But, as usual, she complied with Jacob's demands - he had no idea of course as to the consequences of what he had asked. For surely if he had foreseen the great cost to all his family, he might then have heeded her words and respected her wishes.

THREE
Walker, Northumberland – 1893

Margaret, being only four, had little idea that her mother was heavily pregnant with her eighth child but she was aware that something was happening in the Burns' household. Catherine, her younger sister, no longer slept in the cot but had come to join her in the bed that she already shared with her two older brothers. The boys and girls had to lie at opposite ends of the bed, their feet meeting in the middle. Nothing unusual about this arrangement, it was common practice, though it wasn't very conducive to a good night's sleep.

Margaret also noticed that her mother seemed preoccupied and would usher the children outside every morning, virtually as soon as they were up and dressed, even when it was pouring with rain.

As they were playing in the yard, one afternoon, Margaret heard her mother calling. She was raising her voice and her words alarmed Margaret:

'Walter! Walter! Are you there? I need your help!'

Mary was shouting for Jacob's older cousin who lived next door and fortunately he too had sensed the urgency in her tone and hastily appeared behind the low brick wall that separated the two properties.

'Quick Walter, do you know where a midwife might be found?' Mary gasped, 'Me baby's coming.'

'I'll see to it Mary and I'll go and fetch me wife to take care of your bairns, so don't you be worrying,' he said calmly, trying to reassure her and keep her from panicking.

'Please, please be as quick as you can,' Mary begged as she gripped her stomach, bending over with the intense pain.

The midwife seemed to take an age but when she finally arrived, she rushed upstairs, with Walter not far behind her, and discovered Mary languishing on her bed. She quickly assessed the situation and realised all was not well. Mary was making little progress in delivering her child. Her face was ashen and drops of sweat were running down her brow. Her breathing seemed shallow, her pulse barely recordable and she was in a very distressed state.

'Fetch the doctor Walter!' the midwife spoke sternly and urgently, trying to stay composed.

'He could charge her up to a guinea,' Walter replied, hesitating.

'Just go and fetch the doctor - now!' she reiterated, her voice rising in panic.

Mary was struggling to cope with every contraction. The experienced midwife watched in horror as her 'patient' began to haemorrhage - the flow of blood soaking into the bed linen and trickling down onto the floor. She had no medical training and was at a loss to know how best to staunch the flow. Her attempts at using some cotton rags were proving totally ineffective. She tried to reassure Mary that all would be well but she recognised that this was a life-threatening situation. There was still no sign of the baby's arrival either and realising that Mary had no strength to deliver the child, she feared for its safety too. Sadly, she'd witnessed similar scenes many times before and knew she was powerless to help. So she simply placed a damp cloth on Mary's brow and took hold of her hand, gently squeezing it, as she witnessed Mary's life ebb away.

'Don't feel guilty,' the doctor said reassuringly, when he spoke to her later. 'Nothing could have been done. Mary must have had a uterine tumour to cause that awful loss of blood; then she became too weak to cope with its effects. It's usually impossible to save the baby in such circumstances, there was no more you could have done.'

When Jacob arrived home, having been sent for by Walter, he struggled to come to terms with what had happened. He'd left that morning, having a wife 'with child' and now she was gone, leaving his seven children motherless. There was no new baby to cradle, just two lifeless bodies laid upstairs, awaiting the undertaker.

He was distraught, not just because of his wife's premature death but he had real concerns over the future. His fears were justified, for how would he cope with the demands of a young family, whilst earning the means to keep them? He knew he had no choice but to accept the situation, although telling the children was going to be the first hurdle- and such a difficult one.

'Your ma won't be coming back,' was all he could cope with saying to them, without showing any true emotion. 'She's gone to heaven with the baby.'

'Can't I go there?' Margaret asked naively.

The older children cried bitterly but there was little comfort from their da.

He knew from the outset, that he would have to continue working. No work meant no pay and he couldn't rely on the little income that his oldest son brought in from the pit. There was only one solution to the problem. Nancy, although only fourteen, must now adopt the role of mother, as she was the oldest female sibling. Fortunately, Mary had trained her well in domestic chores and she knew what was required of her. She was not, however, skilled in the role of comforter.

'Shush now!' was all Nancy would say to the sobbing Margaret. But Margaret would not be comforted.

Over the coming weeks and months, the impact of losing her mother was profound. Too young at four to understand why her mother had left her but old enough to miss her presence constantly, she regressed into a spoilt toddler, refusing food and throwing tantrums.

She badgered Nancy persistently, 'Where's me ma gone, why has she not come back yet?' but never received a satisfactory answer.

When on the brief occasions she did see her da, she clung to him, as if frightened that he might disappear too. But he had nothing to give her in the way of comfort. He was struggling in his own way, with the untimely death of his wife. It wasn't so much the child rearing - he was happy for the most part to leave that to Nancy, the exception being the times when they stepped out of line, then he would exert his discipline. But Jacob sorely missed the fulfilment and companionship of married life. He knew of other widowers who expected their oldest daughter to 'warm their bed' but he never considered that to be 'proper'. Over the coming days, he became a restless spirit with a demeanour that was mostly melancholic and serious.

'We're moving again, further south, to Chester-le-Street, at the end of the month,' he announced one weekend, 'I've found new employment there.'

Everyone accepted it without comment - such moves now seemed part of everyday life. Nancy though was becoming equally restless. She was a spirited teenager and yet quite naïve, despite the maturity that had been forced upon her. She began to resent the hours she had to spend on housework and childminding. On many evenings, after putting the younger children to bed, she would slip out of the house for a couple of hours. If Jacob caught her, he would expect to be told precisely where and with whom she was spending her time, although she did her best to avoid him.

In late 1895, when Nancy was seventeen, she was horrified when she realised, with growing alarm, that she was expecting a baby. She now longed to have a mother to turn to but instead had the awful prospect of facing her da.

'Who's responsible for getting you in this mess?' Jacob demanded, when she finally summoned the courage to tell him.

'It's a young lad called Bill Keers who works at the pit.'

In truth he wasn't that young. Aged twenty-seven, he was ten years older than Nancy but to her such facts were irrelevant. She was totally smitten with Bill and had had no thought for what her all-consuming desire might lead to. Now she was paying for it.

'You'll have to be married and soon!' shouted Jacob angrily, 'there's no other way round it... You'll still have to look after the children mind,' he added as an afterthought.

Nancy became rather concerned at this point. Would Bill actually want to commit to her? He'd assured her that he loved her when she told him she was 'with child' but was his love great enough to want to 'adopt' Nancy's ready-made family as well. It was a big ask.

'I love children,' he reassured her, 'I don't mind a house full of them... and I'd like a few of my own too.'

Nancy grinned, she was so relieved to hear this but she wasn't sure if he fully appreciated the extent of his commitment.

On a lovely warm day in July 1896, there was a family wedding. It wasn't a white wedding but 'due to circumstances' it was a quiet simple ceremony conducted at the local parish church. The younger children were excited to get new clothes for the occasion but as it wasn't a cause for celebration, no guests were invited. It was back to work for Bill straight afterwards and for Nancy the endless round of housework continued, despite her impending motherhood.

By September, Nancy had given birth to a baby boy who they decided to name James. Despite his arrival, Nancy continued to act as mother to her younger siblings but it wasn't a role she relished. Although she did her best to hold the family together, maintaining harmony was an on-going problem. With limited time, little money and no experience, Nancy struggled to cope with the demands of her baby as well as the emotional needs of her younger siblings, especially with Margaret and her unpredictable moods. Sometimes Margaret was withdrawn and sullen whilst at others she was loud and demanding, wanting Nancy's support and attention. Nancy now had other priorities and was too exhausted to give her much of her time.

'I'm finding Margaret increasingly difficult to handle,' Nancy complained to her husband, after she'd witnessed Margaret losing her temper yet again and hitting out at Hannah, 'I'm sure it was simply frustration because she didn't get her own way.'

'Just try to ignore her behaviour and leave her be, for the

time being,' he suggested, 'you've enough to deal with, having to look after the baby. She'll have to learn to be more self- reliant and the others will have to learn to stand up to her.'

Nancy followed his advice but it left Margaret feeling increasingly unwanted and she harboured a growing sense of isolation. She convinced herself that now Nancy was married to Bill and had a child of her own, she had lost her place in her sister's affections. No longer did she receive the reassurance of being loved that she so craved. As for her father's love - she had decided that it was lost forever.

FOUR
Chester-le-Street, County Durham - 1899

'I've met a young widow called Marian and I've asked her to marry me,' Jacob announced one Sunday, as he enjoyed his day off from work, relaxing with his family.

The children remained silent, taking a while to register this news, especially with all its implications. But Jacob hadn't finished, there was further, more difficult news to take on board:

'I'm going to live in Witton Gilbert, six mile up the road, with her young family. You'll all stay here with Nancy and Bill. I know they'll take good care of you.'

The family were completely taken aback, they were totally unaware that their father had been meeting anyone and now he was telling them that he was remarrying – and that this woman had children of her own! Margaret, still vulnerable at the best of times, was unable to contain her emotions, and became visibly distressed. After bursting into tears, she stormed out of the house. No one followed after her, although Nancy stood up, intending to do so.

'Leave her be!' Jacob insisted, 'she'll have to get used to idea!'

Margaret sat forlornly on the front doorstep leading onto the cobbled street and buried her face in her hands. A maelstrom of emotions jostled in her head. Life just didn't seem fair. Did no one care about her? She liked being with Nancy and Bill but they had their own bairn to look after. Was she now going to lose her da, as well as her mother? Me da must care more for that woman than he does for me, she mused. I hate him and I hate her even more!

Back inside, Jacob revealed the reasons for his decision to leave his family, trying to justify it. He was sure marrying Marian would be of mutual benefit to them both. He related how they had had an instant connection. He explained that Marian's first husband, Henry, had died, aged thirty-six, of nephritis, a kidney condition that had slowly destroyed his health. Similarly, Jacob had told Marian that he too had lost his wife when she was thirty-six. Yes, Jacob admitted, at forty-four, he was twelve years older than Marian, but it didn't bother either of them. She was in need of a breadwinner to finance herself and her three young children whilst he was in need of a wife to look after him. He had his needs too, like any other man. He was in no doubt that his daughter and son-in-law would willingly continue to look after his own children, especially now they were growing up and becoming more independent. Not like Marian's children, three young boys under six, who still required support and nurture.

Margaret, though, was most definitely bothered by her father's plans. Her resentment of Marian was tangible, even though she had yet to meet her. And now her indignation was towards her father too. Why was he doing this? Didn't he realise, he was making her feel as if she were an orphan.

This was further reinforced, when Nancy told her later that Jacob was not only moving in with this lady but that he would be looking after her three boys. Margaret reasoned that her father's affections must be greater towards these stepchildren than for his own family.

Margaret sulked for many days and secretly hoped her father would change his mind.

But on September 2nd 1899, the marriage took place at the local parish church and Jacob left his family, just as he'd stated, and went to live with Marian and her children.

Fortunately, Bill was able to find better housing to help him provide adequate shelter for his ever-increasing family. He had the opportunity to move into a miner's house in Pelton, a small village just north of Chester-le-Street. He had secured work as a coal-hewer at Pelton Fell mine, under the employment of Mr James Joicey, the local Member of Parliament. Mr Joicey had the reputation of being a fair employer: he paid well and his houses were better than most.

'Good job we have this miner's house, as there'll be nine of us when this next bairn arrives,' Nancy informed him several weeks later, patting her expanding stomach.

'Good job, I'm earning a bit more too,' Bill added, smiling, 'when there'll be nine mouths to feed as well.'

Margaret was determined that she wanted nothing to do with her new stepmother but her father insisted that she go to help Marian look after her younger stepbrothers, at different times in the week. Bitterly resentful, Margaret knew she couldn't refuse. Crossing her father was not an option, besides deep down she knew she loved him and still wanted to see him.

Spending time with Marian soon led Margaret to conclude that her assumptions about her had been partway correct. She thought her stepmother was a hard woman but undoubtedly she would have felt the same about any woman in her position. She was, Margaret conceded, an attractive lady with her dark hair and deep brown eyes but it was her exacting discipline that Margaret found so irksome. She continually dwelt on how different life would be if her real mother, Mary, had still been alive. She might have coped with taking orders from her but she fiercely objected to being bossed around by a woman whom she felt had no right to do so.

Yet, Margaret did have reason to be grateful to Marian and in a most unexpected way.

'Come and help me Margaret,' Marian ordered one evening, 'I've a special job for you.'

Margaret didn't know what was coming but she guessed she wouldn't like it. Off Marian went down the backyard heading for the alleyway, with Margaret dragging behind her. Marian seemed to be in a great hurry, as she quickly grabbed the old tin bucket from the yard and thrust it into Margaret's hand, before marching on. It was a cold winter's night and Margaret was transfixed by the hoarfrost covering the surface of the bucket, as the ice crystals glinted in the moonlight. She was suddenly aware of Marian's voice shouting loudly:

'Keep up! Keep up Margaret! If you don't hurry, it'll happen before we get there.'

Margaret was puzzled. What was she talking about? Needless to say she didn't dare question her or disobey her orders. She quickly followed her stepmother into a neighbour's house. The two of them almost ran up the narrow stairs, leading into a small back bedroom. Margaret was perturbed as she heard the sounds of someone groaning and in obvious distress. On entering the darkened room, she was aware of the figure of a young girl, lying on the bed.

'This is Isabella,' Marian said, 'her husband works down the pit with your da.'

Isabella didn't respond. She was too occupied with her labour.

Margaret had never seen a birth before and was riveted to the spot until her stepmother's loud voice jolted her back to reality.

'Take the bucket, see if you can get some water from the outside tap and put it in the set pot to boil, Margaret.'

Quickly she did as she was told, quite relieved to escape from the sounds and sights that confronted her. On her return she watched mesmerised as the baby boy arrived and was overcome with elation, especially as she was allowed to clean the baby, after witnessing its first cries.

'What are you going to call the child?' she asked Isabella.

'Thomas,' she replied, 'it's a family name.'

'I like it,' Margaret replied, as she placed the child into his mother's arms.

'Well Margaret, you can help me again next time I'm acting as midwife for any neighbours who are in labour,' Marian told her as they returned home.

Margaret wasn't entirely sure she wanted to do this but there was nothing to be gained by disagreeing with her. Gradually though, Margaret became used to helping at home deliveries and an idea began to form in her mind about her future. Maybe she could train as a nurse.

Being a nurse would surely be better than going into domestic service, as so many young girls seemed to do. And it would most definitely be better than getting married and having to stay at home and look after a house full of crying babies and noisy children. To Margaret that seemed sheer drudgery. No, she definitely didn't want to be married and be weighed down by the demands of motherhood. These views were compounded, when Marian went on to have her own baby to Jacob. Eva was born in 1902 and Margaret was frequently asked to act as baby-minder - a situation that she both resented and disliked.

Despite this help given to her stepmother, Margaret was largely ignorant as to how babies were actually conceived and she certainly didn't dare ask. Such subjects - along with any sexual matters - were rarely spoken about. Margaret certainly never considered confiding in Marian or sharing anything too personal with her.

Early one morning, soon after her thirteenth birthday, Margaret went out to the privy in the back yard and was horrified to discover blood seeping down between her legs. In a state of panic, she ran to her older sister for advice:

'I think I've sat on a nail, Nancy, I'm bleeding down below,' she cried.

'Don't be daft,' replied Nancy, 'you've just started your 'monthlies' - it's quite normal and happens to all girls of your age - it's called 'being unwell'. It's also known as every single woman's curse and every married woman's comfort but you'll not understand that just yet,' she said laughing. She looked at Margaret's puzzled face and quickly added: 'Watch out though, for it means you're now capable of having a baby of your own.'

'What! I don't understand!' retorted Margaret, 'How does that happen? Anyway, it won't happen to me. I never want babies - I've had more than enough of looking after Marian's children. Besides, I remember only too well that childbirth caused the death of my dear mother.'

FIVE
Pelton, County Durham - 1902-08

Margaret - although now she'd decided to adopt her preferred name of Maggie - was growing into an extremely attractive young girl. Her very distinctive auburn hair, which curled around her pretty face, was undoubtedly her most striking feature. She had unusual deep green eyes, which added to her beauty and a slim figure, with a developing bosom, which she showed off with great satisfaction. She would choose her clothes carefully and always tried to present herself neatly. Not known for her shyness, Maggie began to really appreciate the male attention her looks brought her. But she was filled with resentment, for she felt trapped by the considerable demands that Marian made on her time and keenly missed the lack of freedom to do as she wished.

She hated the fact that her life was split between living at Pelaw Square with her brothers and sisters in Pelton and then having to make the journey to her stepmother's house in Witton Gilbert, which was a round trip of almost twelve miles. Whilst she was disappointed that she saw little of her father, as he was usually working down the pit when she visited, she felt strongly that she was seeing far too much of her stepmother. This was because Marian required extra help, as she was now expecting a second child to Jacob.

'I don't want to be tied down to looking after children all my life,' Maggie complained to Nancy, 'I have it in mind to work in the local hospital. Then one day, I'll perhaps be able to train as a nurse.'

'Just be patient, you'll be fourteen soon and then you can pursue your idea,' advised Nancy, 'It will be worth the wait as it'll give you the independence you're so desperate to have.'

Maggie had come to respect her sister, especially in her role as surrogate mother. With maturity, she'd realised that Nancy had been too busy having her own family to give her more attention in the past and that it hadn't meant she wasn't loved. She now appreciated her more as a friend, turning to her for advice and thinking of her as an ally in her battle to gain freedom from Marian's demands. She listened to what Nancy had suggested, bided her time and then applied, successfully, to work in her local hospital as a nursing attendant. She enjoyed the daily routine, the interaction with the patients and certainly the wage at the end of the week, which, although minimal, gave her some feeling of self-worth.

Most of her meagre earnings she gave to William and Nancy but she was allowed to keep a little for her own personal needs. Her spare time was still limited but when opportunity did allow, she just loved to go dancing. This was a chance to meet up with old friends and also to make new ones, particularly lads. Marian frowned on such activities - to her dancing was frivolous, even immoral.

'It's not proper for a young lady to be parading herself, ' chided her stepmother, 'only 'light women' do that!'

Now brave enough to stand up for herself, Maggie didn't care what her stepmother thought, or anyone else for that matter. Life was for living and she intended to enjoy herself. She'd spent too long being miserable in the past. As she matured, the more she realised there were opportunities out there for the pursuit of pleasure and she was keen to discover them and have fun. Why should it be a girl's misfortune, to be tied down to housework and child rearing? It seemed to Maggie that boys had all the opportunities for amusement. They had their sport such as football and cricket and their greyhound and whippet racing. They had the choice of playing in brass bands or singing in various choirs. When they were older they could escape to the hostelry, play a game of dominoes and enjoy some company and time away from work and family. It struck Maggie that women had no opportunity for such activities and girls were simply expected to spend their days in domestic drudgery. Surely, Maggie concluded, a girl was entitled to some freedom and a chance to relax away from the demands of everyday life in the home.

That summer, with this burgeoning attitude, Maggie began to rebel and follow her own desires. She horrified her stepmother when she announced,

'I've entered the beauty queen competition at the next gala day.'

'Why would you want to parade yourself like that?' Marian asked in disbelief.

'Because I think I stand a good chance of winning,' she replied rather rudely.

'I don't know what your da will have to say, when he hears what you're planning,' Marian continued.

'Maybe, he'll be proud of me when I win,' Maggie said with satisfaction.

The miner's gala was an annual event in the city, held on the second Saturday in July. Everyone looked forward to it. It was a great social occasion and a chance for all the pitmen to spend time with their families. The Durham Miner's Gala – 'The Big Meeting' - was the biggest in the area and many folk from the surrounding villages went along to support it. A brass band provided the musical entertainment and there was a procession through the city, led by representatives of each colliery, holding aloft their individual banner. They marched to the Racecourse and listened to political speeches from their union leaders and MPs and it even provided a chance to air their grievances. Maggie felt she would like to join them, she'd surely have plenty to say.

She was truly delighted when her words were fulfilled and she was crowned as the gala queen for that year. Although winning was a great prize, the defiance she felt against her stepmother, was an even better feeling. It also raised her self-esteem. No longer, the little orphan girl that nobody cared about, she was, she told herself, an attractive teenager and the boys better watch out!

Three years later...

Knowing it was the best place for couples to meet, the street was now Maggie's social scene. She never missed an opportunity to go out walking for pleasure on a Sunday, either alone or with one of her fellow nursing attendants. Young men were her target audience, she thoroughly enjoyed their company and certainly appreciated the attention they gave her. She always ensured that she looked her best, wearing her smartest dress and a matching bonnet. She tried to be courteous and amusing, knowing that politeness and a sense of humour were attractive features to have. Yet she didn't want boys to think of her as too forward, they may just get the wrong idea. Nor did she wish them to think of her as needy or immature, she could certainly stand up for herself and knew her own mind.

'I've spotted a right good-looking lad today, Nancy. I've certainly not seen him before,' she told her sister excitedly one summer evening. 'I'm not sure how to approach him, without appearing too keen.'

'Just talk to him naturally, the next time you see him,' suggested Nancy, 'I know you're not shy at coming forward but make sure you spend time listening to what he has to say and take an interest in his family.'

The following weekend, Maggie went out as usual, hoping she'd have the chance to follow her sister's advice. She was delighted when she came across her 'good looking lad' once again. They stopped to talk. He was friendly and open and Margaret sensed that the attraction she felt was mutual. Neither of them was reserved and conversation flowed easily.

'I've not seen you around before,' Maggie commented, blushing slightly as she added, 'and I'm wondering what I've been missing.'

'Well, that's because I've only recently moved here from Holmside, to work in the local pit,' he explained.

'I'm pleased you did,' Maggie said smiling, 'I'm Maggie Burns, by the way... what's your name?'

' John-George Purvis, by the way, ' he teased.

'Have you come with family?' she continued, remembering to follow Nancy's instructions. She was also eager to ascertain if he'd a sweetheart already... or a wife even.

'Aye,' he replied, 'I'm living with me parents and me seven brothers and sisters.'

'I've six brothers and sisters too,' Maggie told him, 'but I don't have a ma or a da at home.

'You're not in charge, are you, of that many bairns?' John-George enquired, showing concern.

'What are you saying? That I'm not old enough? I am seventeen,' she said with great conviction. 'But no, I have an older married sister that looks after us... or at least tries to.'

'I'm twenty one, but I still need looking after at times,' John-George joked and both of them laughed.

Maggie couldn't help but notice that he had the most wonderful expressive face with a captivating smile and the deepest of green eyes. He was small in stature, not much taller than she was but he had a good physique with strong, broad shoulders. He looked smart in his Sunday best clothes and he had the air of a gentleman with his homemade walking stick, an essential accessory for all fashionable young men. She found herself excited by him.

Maggie herself was thought of as 'quite a catch' by most of the local lads, with her striking auburn hair and her matching colourful personality. Somehow she had an air of mystery about her and John-George was more than eager to make her acquaintance.

'Do you fancy going out walking with me?' he asked 'and then you'll find out just what it is you've been missing.'

Maggie hesitated but not for long.

'I'd love to,' she told him, 'that is I'd love to go for a walk,' but then added rather coyly, 'maybe then I can find out just what it is that you're referring to.'

'Where do you work?' John-George enquired, wanting to know how soon she could have a day off.

'I'm an attendant at the hospital but I usually have Sundays as my free day.'

'Let's meet next Sunday then, same time, same place,' he suggested.

'I'll look forward to it, thank you', she said politely, keeping her distance, although in truth she wanted to reach over and kiss him there and then.

That evening, she couldn't wait to share her good fortune with Nancy.

'I'm happy for you Maggie, but please watch yourself, you know what I've told you before, about going with a lad and then having his babies.'

Maggie laughed, 'And I've told you, I'm not interested in having babies - ever. Besides, I'm a decent girl, even if Marian tells you differently.'

The following Sunday, the pair met and spent the time getting to know each other better. Maggie shared her past and all the pain it had caused her. She told him of her sadness at never really knowing her own mother and the resentment she felt towards her stepmother. She even felt relaxed enough to disclose that even though she worked in a hospital, she dreamt of becoming an actress, for she loved the idea of performing on stage. She had no desire to be tied down to a life of domestic servitude; she wanted to be adventurous, daring even.

'Maggie Burns, I think you're a bit of a rebel, aren't you,' John-George remarked after he'd listened to her patiently. 'You remind me of those women that everyone's talking about - the Suffragettes - I think they're called, the ones that are wanting more rights for women.'

'Good for them is what I say,' Maggie replied.

John-George – a miner through and through, didn't mock her ideas, despite the fact he'd been brought up to view all women as subordinate. Her outlook was refreshing and he was simply entranced by her. He couldn't wait to meet up again and she was equally delighted that she'd found someone who would listen and not just dismiss her ideas as those of a whimsical girl.

In no time at all they were both chasing any opportunity to meet- not easy when they worked such long hours but nothing was going to stop them. It was not long before John-George suggested that he introduce her to his family.

'I'd like you to meet my mother and father, John and Ann, plus all my brothers and sisters. They're sure to like you Maggie and they've heard nothing else from me these past few weeks, but talk of you!'

Maggie told him that she'd be really happy to do that but she wasn't too sure what to expect, especially as John-George had warned her that his father had a bit of a temper. When the day arrived for the arranged visit, she entered the house rather tentatively. His father did seem rather scary with his huge white beard but she needn't have been concerned for he turned out to be pleasant enough and spoke to her kindly. Maggie could see from whom John-George had inherited his good looks for, despite his advancing years, he still had very piercing eyes, which were a rich emerald in colour.

The house was full of family, just like hers back home. There were two older brothers, Thomas and Henry, plus an older sister Jane.

'Call her Jenny though not Jane,' laughed John-George as he introduced her.

'I'll never remember these names,' Margaret remarked, although she was later to come to depend on Jenny in a way she would never have imagined.

'These are my little sisters, although they're not so little now,' he continued. 'Isabella, Esther, Dorothy and finally your namesake, Margaret. '

'Yes but I'm a Meg, not a Maggie,' his youngest sister piped up, smiling.

On her way back home that night, Maggie felt both uplifted and sad. She realised just how happy a complete, close knit family could be and they'd made her feel such a part of it. Yet this was something that she'd never truly known since her mother had died. The pain of her loss still smarted despite the passing of the years.

Her thoughts raced as she began to realise just how much John-George was coming to mean to her. Would it be presumptuous to tell him? At seventeen, would he think her too young to be getting serious?

'I like your family,' she paused, 'and I think I'm falling for you!' she whispered as they said their goodbyes outside her home.

'Then, I better hold on to you lass,' he replied, gently putting his arm around her waist and pulling her close.

Maggie leaned forward and kissed him with intensity. John-George was totally mesmerised and could hardly believe his good fortune. He was sure that he'd captured the heart of the best looking girl in the village.

From that evening onwards, the two of them became virtually inseparable. Their feelings for each other grew intense and uncontrollable. Maggie knew only too well that you were meant to wait, intimacy was only for married couples, at least that's what she'd had drummed into her. Her intentions were good, she knew what was expected of her, but her desire was too great. Finding themselves alone one evening, their hurried fumbling soon led to a bodily union, which despite its brevity gave Maggie a pleasure that she had never experienced before.

There was certainly no regret that evening - the regret was to come in the weeks ahead when it dawned on Maggie that there were consequences to her actions. Normally she would have confided her fears to Nancy but first she wanted to gauge John-George's reaction. Would he still want her and would he be prepared to commit?

SIX
Bowburn - 1908

Maggie was greatly relieved to discover that John-George was more than happy to stay with her, despite her belief that she was expecting a child. In fact his reaction was much more positive than she could have hoped for,

'Let's get married and soon,' John-George suggested, 'no child of mine is going to be a bastard. There's no room at my family's home and certainly not at yours but I'll try to find us a miner's cottage to rent, so we can be our own little family.'

Maggie was delighted and sufficiently encouraged to be able to face her family. She recalled her father's reaction when Nancy had told him she was 'with child' but she was more audacious than her sister. Even if he wasn't happy, she was determined now that her future life was with John-George.

Nancy soon confirmed that Maggie's symptoms were that of an expectant mother and she reminded her that there was no going back:

'What's done is done,' she remarked in her typically blunt manner, 'so best get on with it! It'll be hard work and you'll have to give up your dreams of becoming a nurse but...

'I hadn't thought of that,' Maggie said with some sadness and then added, with her typical feelings of injustice, 'It seems so unfair that you have to give up your employment, once you get married.'

'You won't be the first girl to think that,' Nancy replied, 'and I'm sure you won't be the last. You better go and tell Jacob and Marian your news, you'll soon not be able to hide it and you can't be expected to help much longer with their young 'uns. You'll certainly have no time once you've a bairn of your own.'

Maggie decided to call at Witton Gilbert, that very week. It was early evening by the time she had walked from work and she was greatly relieved to find both Jacob and Marian at home. When she broke the news that she was expecting a baby and that a wedding had been arranged, her father's response was totally unexpected.

'It seems like we'll be having two family weddings then,' was his only comment.

'Why's that?' Maggie asked puzzled.

'Your sister Hannah has just informed us that she's marrying her Albert, at Holy Trinity Church, in September. But then she's in no rush, as she's not in the family way.'

Maggie ignored his sarcasm and was quite relieved that he didn't seem particularly angry. Or did his apparent indifference simply indicate that he was no longer really interested in her?

'We were thinking we'd arrange our marriage for July,' Maggie continued, 'are you willing to be there?'

'Alright, lass,' was all he said and Maggie decided she'd leave it at that.

Just a few months later, on July 5th, a very short ceremony was held at Holy Trinity, the parish church in Pelton. The congregation merely consisted of members of the two families, with the bride's father and the parish clerk, Mr. William Craine, acting as the two witnesses.

Maggie chose to wear a bonnet and a simple cotton dress, with a long full skirt, hoping it would suitably hide her bulging waistline from any onlookers who might be waiting outside. Not that she felt any great shame at her condition, for wasn't she marrying the man she loved and that surely couldn't be deemed 'promiscuous.'

Afterwards, there were none of the usual celebrations for the newly-weds. There was no family meal, no iced wedding cake and no boiled ham and pease pudding to enjoy. Her da wouldn't hear of it. John-George had to return to work straightaway and Maggie was left alone to begin her role as a dutiful wife.

John-George had been true to his word. Because he worked in Sherburn colliery, he'd managed to secure a rented miner's cottage at 2, West Sherburn, on the outskirts of Durham City. As Maggie stood in the small parlour, surveying her surroundings, the reality of what she had done, hit her almost immediately. The house appeared adequate for their needs but it certainly didn't feel like home. The silence was almost unbearable. Used to the constant noise of family life, with its endless banter and never ending activity, Maggie suddenly felt very alone. She was aware that she knew nobody in the village and yet what chance would she have to make anyone's acquaintance? Being heavily pregnant meant she was unable to venture very far.

Over the following days, as the final weeks of her confinement were upon her, even basic tasks began to be a problem. Maggie's back ached from the constant need to fetch water and she struggled to cope with the endless pile of laundry. The heat of the day proved exhausting and by nighttime, she had no energy left to prepare a meal for John-George. Sleep eluded her as the limited space of the narrow double bed brought great discomfort. As every morning passed, it became harder to rouse herself in time to see to her husband's needs.

It was just six weeks after the wedding that she awoke one morning and felt a sharp pain searing through her body. Aware that John-George was already up, she forced herself downstairs to prepare his bait and tin can of cold tea. She'd quickly learnt that he expected jam sandwiches, as the sweetness of them was a well-known antidote against the coal dust, which made food lack flavour. But on this occasion there was no jam in the cupboard. She cursed aloud and then without warning, the pain shot through her body again. The many times she'd helped Marian to deliver babies gave her an idea of what was happening.

'John-George! John-George!' she cried out, 'Please don't go off to work just yet, as I'm sure the baby is on the way!'

'I'll go and summon the midwife,' he replied and with that he was gone.

Maggie went to lie on her bed and tried to battle through the intense pain of the contractions, knowing her body was young and well able to cope with them. As they grew in severity, she tried hard not to panic. She was relieved when she heard the sound of John-George returning with the midwife. Realising there was little he could do, he went off to work.

On his return, several hours later, he was delighted to discover Maggie had given him a son. On entering the room, seeing his first child lying in his wife's arms, John-George was overcome with emotion.

'Shall we name him Jacob, after my father?' Maggie suggested wearily and John-George nodded - at that moment he would have agreed to any name.

He was transfixed by his new son and marvelled at his perfectly formed body, particularly his tiny fingers and toes.

'He's going to have your hair colour, that's for certain,' he told Maggie as he studied Jacob's fine strands of red hair, ' and he has a good pair of lungs, like you too,' he kidded, as Jacob cried lustily.

Maggie was pleased to see John-George so happy but inwardly she was quite troubled. She wondered whether she was ready for motherhood, knowing a baby brought added responsibilities and needed long term commitment. Was this an end to all her hopes and desires and the start of a life in which she would experience pregnancy every eighteen months or so, just like her mother before her. She had wanted more from life than that. But she tried to stay positive, knowing that she had a good man in John-

George who was much more understanding than a lot of husbands.

'I've some good news for you lass,' John-George announced soon after Jacob's birth, 'I've been offered a transfer to a new pit at Bowburn.'

Throughout Britain, the demand for coal was increasing, especially with the growth of new towns such as Middlesbrough and the flourishing iron and steel industry in Teesside. This, in turn, had led to a growth in colliery villages. John-George worked for Bell Brothers, who were local landowners and he thought of them as reputable, honest employers. They'd recently decided to open a new, ultra-modern colliery in Bowburn where initially they had employed a hundred men, averaging an output of six hundred tons of coal every day. But now, John-George had been told, with demand growing, they were looking for more men to take on. He was really keen to give it a go,

'I'm sure you'll like it there,' he re assured his wife, 'it's better...'

'Oh no!' Maggie interrupted, 'do you realise how many times I've moved house in my life? We've just got settled here and what with the new baby, I really can't face a house move.'

'But it's better pay - twenty six shillings a week, plus a free bag of coal, we've got to consider it at least,' he insisted.

Reluctantly Maggie agreed, realising it was too good an opportunity to miss.

Confirmation came that it was the right decision when Maggie saw her newly built miner's cottage, at number 1, Wylam Street. She was delighted. The four rooms, two bedrooms upstairs and a small kitchen and living room downstairs seemed relatively spacious. There was also a large outside cement yard with a brick built privy.

'I think I'm going to like it here,' she said, hugging John-George in appreciation, 'I hope we'll be able to settle and stay here for a good few years.'

An added bonus was that it was within a stone's throw of her in- laws who lived down the same street at number nineteen. Maybe, she told herself, this would also lift her spirits and provide her with some much needed company and support.

It took Maggie a while to adapt to her husband's new shift pattern which involved being woken and having to prepare food, at all hours of the day and night but slowly she settled down into her role as a miner's wife. She looked forward to pay day, on the last working day of each week, when she'd wait outside the front door, with her apron ready in position, so that John-George could place his wages in her pocket. Maggie liked to have the money. She knew if John-George had charge of it, more would be spent at the alehouse. This way, she had control of the finances and she was disciplined in making sure the baby's needs for food and clothes were her priority, although she was finding it increasingly difficult to make the money stretch to the end of the week.

She'd come to terms with the fact that she had to forgo her dream to be a nurse but she still found it very hard to accept that being a full time housewife and mother was every married woman's lot. The necessity to constantly cook, clean and wash on a daily basis had been largely ingrained into her since early childhood but it still irked her that it dominated her life.

Neither were the demands of a new baby easy to cope with. Maggie felt restricted, having lost her independence and was overcome with weariness by the end of the day. She began to wish that she'd waited to have a child and not allowed herself to get carried away that first night. Even the intimacy with John-George, didn't seem so exciting, now she knew it had consequences. Maggie did not always want to give herself to her husband when he made his demands after a night in the alehouse.

'Come on now Maggie, a man needs his comforts,' John-George would say, but Maggie was constantly fearful of the outcome.

'I just can't face another baby at the moment - it's hard enough to look after the bairn we have already, let alone find the money to feed 'im, without another on the way,' she pleaded.

But John-George had his way, and by the end of 1909, Maggie found herself expecting a second child.

'You're going to be a da again,' she informed him just before Christmas.

Maggie tried to carry on her normal life but she struggled with sickness and extreme tiredness. John-George, a typical man of that time, never considered helping her with either the domestic chores or looking after Jacob, even as she grew in size.

Maggie certainly appreciated when one of John-George's sisters called round.

'Would you like a hand with the laundry?' Jenny suggested, as she saw Maggie struggling to heave sodden sheets out of the old poss tub one Monday morning.

'Why that'd be a great help,' Maggie sighed and smiled weakly.

'I could do with you watching Jacob too as he's into everything and I must watch he doesn't get too close to the boiling water. I'll be glad when he's old enough to go outside and play by himself.'

'It'll happen soon enough,' Jenny assured her, 'they're not babies for long. I'll come round and give you a hand when the next baby arrives if you like.'

'I'd really appreciate that,' Maggie answered, 'I'm hoping it's a girl… who'll maybe not be quite such a handful.'

Jenny simply smiled sympathetically in response.

Early one July morning, Maggie recognised a familiar pain and realised the baby was on its way.

'Don't you go to work just yet,' she begged John-George, 'afore you do, please fetch Mrs Smith and hurry!'

Her husband rushed off but to Maggie it seemed an age before he came back.

'I'm here now,' Mrs Smith told her calmly, 'No need to panic. Let's see how you're doing,' and with that she ordered Maggie to lie on the bed.

Maggie tried to stay calm despite the onslaught of a recurring pain that seemed to sear through her lower body.

'It's nearly here,' Mrs Smith claimed, although Maggie didn't believe her.

Maggie then reached for a cloth and forced it between her lips, biting hard into it, to try and relieve some of the agony whilst Mrs Smith went off to boil some water and find a few clean towels.

Just as she departed, Maggie became aware of the baby's imminent arrival. She called out but with that the child appeared, in a sudden rush.

'It's a girl!' Mrs Smith exclaimed as she returned to find the baby lying on the bed and upon hearing those words, Maggie allowed some tears to fall.

It was July 13th, 1910, less than two years since the birth of Jacob.

'I'm so happy to have a daughter, this time,' she told her husband, who'd been waiting outside until the birth was over. 'Should we name her Ann, after your mother?'

'I like that idea,' John-George replied, 'for she does have the Purvis look with her dark hair,' he added, as he proudly admired his new child.

For a moment, Maggie dearly wished her own mother had been around to share her joy but then told herself she had no right to be miserable. As they both looked down on their beautiful daughter, she reminded herself how fortunate she was to have safely given birth to two healthy children.

Ann turned out to be the placid baby she had hoped for and Maggie found her generally easy to look after. Jacob, too, seemed to instantly love his sister and would spend time playing with her.

Maggie settled into motherhood and generally took pride in looking after her children. She appreciated having help and gladly welcomed John-George's family, especially Jenny, whenever they cared to drop by. She was disappointed to see little of her own father and even wished her stepmother would call occasionally and show some interest in her family.

There were still days however, which didn't go well, as Jacob seemed such an independent little boy with a strong will.

'I don't know where he gets his temper from,' Maggie moaned to John-George, after she'd reacted badly to yet another temper tantrum and smacked him.

'I do,' said John-George ruefully, staring hard at her.

'Yes, of course, it's your dad's fault,' she retorted. And then they both laughed.

Maggie enjoyed it when they could share a giggle and John-George certainly appreciated her mischievous sense of fun, especially when it overshadowed the more melancholic side to her nature that he attributed to her difficult childhood.

For the next few months, this was how life seemed to be - a mixture of highs and lows - but she accepted this, realising that you had to take the bad with the good in life, just as long as they balanced themselves out.

Rarely did her life extend beyond Bowburn and its surrounding villages but this did not trouble her. She was happy to be settled, hoping John-George would stay put at the Bowburn colliery. She was concerned when events suggested otherwise.

'We've all been called on to strike,' he announced unexpectedly, on returning from his shift one day in January 1912, 'and it'll be the first national strike ever!' he exclaimed.

Maggie was shocked, 'What's it all about?' she asked anxiously.

'All us miners, throughout the land, are hoping to secure a minimum wage, for both the pitmen and the boys, as at the moment we're one of the few industries with no basic wage,' he explained.

Maggie was worried, thinking his temporary loss of wages would cause them great hardship, as they had no savings to fall back on. Worse still, could he even forfeit his job?

'Don't you be worrying Maggie,' he reassured her, 'I'll get some strike pay and it'll be worth it in long run. If, as a result of the strike, we end up with increased money every month, you'll be happy then.'

Maggie realised the miners had a right to demand more, knowing that a coal hewer's work was so hard and dangerous. She also understood more of the reasons behind the strike after John-

George explained the unfairness of the present system .It was, he said, the price of coal alone that dictated the amount of pay the miners took home. Unfortunately the majority of coal mined in Durham went overseas, where the market price was very unpredictable and when prices dropped, so did the wages.

The strike was scheduled to begin on the first day of March. As the day approached, John-George tried to make light of it, hoping to reassure his wife and encourage her to stay positive.

'To keep the pit lads occupied and the pit ponies exercised, there's going to be races held at Durham Racecourse, would you like to go?' he asked, 'There'll even be bookmakers there, if you fancy a gamble.'

'Money's too tight already to be thinking of that!' Maggie replied sharply but then she conceded, 'I suppose it'll make a good day out and take our minds off our worries, as long as we don't spend any money.'

So it was agreed and all the family enjoyed a relaxing day out but it didn't stop Margaret fretting every day the strike continued.

Thirty-seven days after its start, the strike was finally over.

'The government's agreed to pass a minimum wages law,' John-George informed Maggie, 'so it's back to work for us all next week.'

Maggie was very relieved to hear life would soon return to normality. But just a fortnight later, an event happened, that caused the hardship and disruption of the strike, to pale into insignificance. News came in that shocked the country as a whole. On April 15th, an ocean going liner, The Titanic, which at the time was the largest passenger ship ever made, had sunk with the loss of hundreds of lives. Its impact was far reaching on both sides of The Atlantic and even Maggie was forced to confront her deepest fears. She tried to imagine how she would have coped, if it had been her husband or one of the children, who had been involved. She chided herself for her fears over money when there were such bigger issues in life to deal with. She truly hoped that she'd never have to suffer the pain of losing a loved one, ever again. She didn't remember her mother but she recognised that the effect of her loss had been profound. She must, she told herself, enjoy her children and show them and John-George how much she loved them. She smiled as she knew what that entailed - she couldn't wait for John-George to come home that night…

Margaret wasn't surprised when a few weeks later she realised she was having a third child. The now familiar feeling of nausea swept over her every morning when she awoke but she accepted it as just one of the ordeals of mother hood which had to be endured. She reminded herself that the sickness only usually lasted for the first few months, plus she was eager to work out when the baby might be due:

'This could be a Christmas baby, I reckon,' Maggie announced ruefully to her husband.

'That will be special, won't it,' he answered with his usual positive spin on things.

But Christmas came and went and it was early January before Maggie delivered a seemingly healthy boy.

'Shall we call him Roland - just to be a bit different this time,' John-George suggested and Maggie happily agreed.

Roland had Maggie's distinctive red hair but he seemed to have John-George's more placid nature. He was a happy, contented baby and Maggie was grateful that he rarely caused her any trouble. However, as the days passed, he developed a weak chest and Maggie began to fret over him as he coughed continuously.

'I wish we'd money put by for some medicine - he needs cough syrup or a poultice at least,' Maggie told John-George, recalling her basic hospital training.

'I'll do what I can to find an extra sixpence from somewhere Maggie but you know how tight money is,' John-George said kindly, recognising his son's need.

Maggie looked at her husband affectionately, appreciating his concern. She could see his dilemma- she knew how hard he worked and how quickly his wages disappeared. But despite this endless cycle of work generated by their young family, plus the financial burden it created, Maggie knew they had a deep and growing love for each other. She was happy to be his wife, even if times were hard, for he showed moments of great tenderness and affection towards her. It was especially appreciated, as she was aware of some husbands who treated their wives badly, even cruelly. She enjoyed being wanted and needed by him, although she was not so pleased with the effect this last pregnancy had on her body. She noticed she was losing the figure she took such pride in and her face showed signs of tiredness and neglect. Having three children under five, was the very situation she had vowed to avoid and she was adamant she didn't want any more children. They couldn't afford it anyway. She must insist that John-George be more careful.

Maggie was pleased that she was now making friends in the village with the other miner's wives. She chatted together with other mothers and encouraged Jacob and Ann to play out in the street with their children.

Day to day living might be monotonous but Maggie had learnt to accept it, knowing it was the same for everyone. Similarly, times of public sorrow or celebration were shared by everyone, not that they came along very often.

'I hear that Queen Mary's coming through the village soon,' one of the well- educated mothers announced. 'I've read, in the Durham Advertiser, that she's travelling from the miner's home in Coxhoe to Durham but coming via Bowburn.'

'Should we all get together and line the streets?' another mother suggested and everyone agreed that it was just what they needed to add some excitement to their rather dull lives.

'Can we go? Can we go?' Ann asked excitedly.

'Do you think she'll wave to you lass?' Jacob teased, although he was glad to hear he was allowed an official day off from school.

Maggie really began to appreciate living within this close knit community. She came to realise there was always help at hand and she only had to knock on the wall and her adjoining neighbour would be there to find out what the problem was. Gradually, Maggie began to trust those around her. Not that she'd share anything too personal. That was not the accepted thing. People's private lives were kept as that. There was, it seemed an unwritten rule: 'Mind your own business and leave folks to mind theirs.'

She couldn't help but notice that one of her neighbours had a black eye one morning. No doubt down to her husband's drink problem, Maggie concluded. But, nothing was said - Maggie had learnt that if you wanted to stay popular you didn't gossip.

The summer of 1914, though, was different, there was gossip and on quite a scale...

SEVEN
Bowburn - Summer 1914

Bowburn had begun to buzz with speculation but this wasn't the usual subject matter - not something personal or about a particular wayward family, rather talk of something that was about to impact on everyone. Rumours abounded and there was a palpable air of expectation and foreboding. What was it all regarding? War! Talk of England going to war with Germany.

'What's a war daddy?' four-year-old Ann asked her father, on hearing her parents talk of it.

'Guns and fighting!' teased Jacob.

'Stop it Jacob!' Maggie yelled, 'It's nowt for you to worry about Ann,' her mother reassured her, fearing that she might have nightmares.

But inwardly Maggie was worried and once they were alone she asked John-George if he could explain what had happened to cause all this talk of war.

'It seems that earlier this week, German troops crossed the frontier into Belgium, intending to march into and attack France. By doing this they've broken some treaty or other and so our government issued them with an ultimatum - either retreat or we'll send in our troops.'

'And did they refuse?' questioned Maggie.

'Aye lass, they did, so now we're officially at war with them,' John-George continued.

'It won't affect us though, will it?' she asked him, anxiously.

'No, it won't impact on us miners up north,' John-George said trying to calm her, ' it'll be up to the regular army to kick them Huns into touch.'

Maggie was temporarily reassured but during early September, she began to notice posters appearing around the village, on every street corner and even on the pillar-box. Posters emblazoned with Lord Kitchener's hand - he was Secretary of State for War - pointing an outstretched finger, demanding 'Your country needs you' and asking all young men, aged between nineteen and thirty, to consider joining the armed services.

'You have to be five foot eight to apply,' John-George told her after she mentioned it.

'So that rules you out,' she quickly retorted, with an inner sigh of relief.

Although Maggie and John-George never had the means to buy one, they were informed that the local newspaper - the Durham Advertiser - was also advertising for recruits. Within days, new headlines appeared, stating that nearly ninety percent of the soldiers in the regular army had been killed or injured in the fight and now additional help was required. The government were after volunteers to form a 'new army.'

'I've been told that's quite unusual,' John-George explained to his puzzled wife, 'no other nation has an army made up of volunteers. But they're keen for all us young men to fight for King and country.'

'What do you mean 'us' - you can't join up, can you?' Maggie asked fearfully.

'It seems they've just decided to lower the height restrictions, hoping to recruit more men. . You only have to be five foot five to qualify, so that rules me back in. I have a conscience Maggie and it tells me I should be patriotic and join up,' John-George continued.

'Yes and you have a young family to support – don't you have a conscience about that too?' Maggie persisted in exasperation.

'Loads of lads are volunteering, Maggie, many of them with family just like us and that hasn't stopped them. I even hear some under age boys are going along to the recruiting office, they're that keen to sign on. They say it's going to be quite an adventure going abroad for the first time. They'll see sights they've never experienced before.'

'Aye and maybe sights that they don't want to see,' Maggie remarked, 'it is a war after all.'

'You're quite right,' John-George admitted and they both agreed to drop the subject for a while but he would, he decided, still give it the careful consideration it deserved.

Over the next few days he talked it over with other colliery men from his village. There were some who were reluctant to sign up but this was due to their religious beliefs. John-George quickly learnt that they earned no respect from the majority of folk and were even threatened with punishment,

' I hear them 'conchies' will get imprisoned if they refuse to do any war work,' John-George informed Maggie, 'I don't wish to be classed as one of them.'

Maggie, reluctantly, tried to come to terms with what John-George was telling her. There were reminders everywhere of the call to arms. Even on a trip to the shop, she was confronted by a pipe band parading around the village in an effort to encourage recruits. She was slowly realising the strength of patriotic feeling, not just in Bowburn, but in the surrounding district and no doubt, she guessed, in the whole country. She'd been told of the arrival of horses and carts, along with food and ammunition at the Durham Racecourse, which had caused great excitement yet it had serious implications. For Maggie, it finally sank in, that this war was going to effect the whole nation, including Durham miners and everyone's support was needed, including that of the wives. She began to feel guilty that she was withholding her support but the prospect of her husband's departure scared her. How would she cope financially and emotionally and how would the children be without their father?

'Why don't you talk it over with your elder brother Henry,' Maggie suggested. 'He's in a similar position to you and I wonder what his thoughts are about signing up?'

'I think that's a good idea,' John-George agreed, 'I'll call round to see him after my shift tomorrow.'

The next evening Maggie was waiting impatiently for John-George's return. She was keen to hear what Henry intended to do and secretly hoped he might have dissuaded John-George from volunteering, for a while at least.

'We've had our decision made for us,' John-George told her as soon as he stepped in the house.

'How do you mean, made for you? ' Maggie enquired with some foreboding.

'Our employers, Bell Brothers, have issued a statement today and it's given us the impetus we needed. We've been promised that they'll keep our mining jobs available for when we return, and you won't have to struggle because I'll be paid seven shillings a week, which you'll be able to collect personally. You'll also be entitled to a free bag of coal every week, which is a generous offer.'

'Does that mean your mind's made up then?' Maggie asked with resignation. 'Both you and Henry are definitely going to enrol?'

'Yes we are,' her husband responded sympathetically, but hoping to ease his guilt he quickly added, 'at least you can stay put and not have your life disrupted by another move.'

'But I'll not manage on seven shillings,' Maggie persisted.

'You'll be entitled to a separation allowance as well, the government are going to give money to all soldier's wives. I reckon it's going to be twelve and six, at least that's what I've been told.'

Maggie felt some consolation but she wasn't prepared for

how quickly things moved forward. The following day John-George, along with Henry, found themselves queuing up, with many other Bowburn miners outside the Literary Institute, which was acting as the local recruiting office, in the nearby village of Coxhoe.

Most of the men were accepted on the spot but there was some banter as a few were rejected on health grounds, after failing a medical. One of John-George's pals was turned away simply because he had bad teeth.

'I didn't think I needed to bite them Huns,' he joked to those waiting in the queue, although in reality he was dreading telling his family he'd been turned away. He didn't want to be mistaken for a coward. He was aware of a custom recently established in the local villages, where angry women would thrust a white feather into your lapel if you were spotted in the street out of uniform. To be on the receiving end of one was something he certainly didn't want, so he was determined to reapply in a few weeks' time.

Neither Henry nor John-George had any problems with their medical and both were accepted on the spot as privates in the Infantry. Henry joined the thirteenth battalion of the Durham Light Infantry whilst John-George joined the tenth, both signing up for the duration of the war. For this, they were rewarded with the King's shilling.

John-George was happy with his decision and decided to treat himself to a packet of his favourite untipped cigarettes - Woodbines - which didn't go down too well with Maggie.

'It could have gone towards some new shoes for the kids!' she argued, but John-George was unrepentant. It was his reward so why shouldn't he spend it on himself.

His initial euphoria was soon replaced by sadness and a certain apprehension when a month after his recruitment, he was informed that he had to journey to Aldershot to undertake a period of training.

The night before he left, Maggie clung to John-George with such intensity that it aroused both their passions. They enjoyed a deeply satisfying union but neither of them dared think it may be their last.

'I love you Maggie Purvis,' John-George whispered, 'I shall dream of you every night whilst I'm away.'

Maggie couldn't respond. She lay, looking up at the ceiling, contemplating the days ahead, trying to come to terms with what was about to happen. Her voice was barely audible when finally she spoke,

'I don't want you to go,' she pleaded. 'Please don't leave me,

I can't bear it.'

'Shush now,' he said as he wrapped his arms around her, 'Let's enjoy this moment and not think of what might be to come.'

Maggie watched as John-George's eyes closed and he fell silent but although she tried to relax and allow sleep to envelop her, her anxiety prevented it. Instead, she allowed her imagination to wander into dark places, picturing her husband succumbing to terrible injuries. She wanted to wake him and be comforted but he was so soundly asleep, she thought better of it. Eventually exhaustion took over and her torment was relieved by slumber.

The next morning, the whole family had to be up just after dawn.

'We're going to Newcastle this morning,' John-George informed Jacob who was grumbling over being awoken so early.

'We're all going to say goodbye to your da,' Maggie continued.

'Why? Where's he going?' questioned their bemused son.

'I've to go down south to be trained as a soldier,' his father explained.

'Do you have to go?' Jacob asked feeling quite dejected.

'Put it like this son, it's up to everyone to help defeat those Germans. We want to show them who's boss.'

'When will you be coming back?' Jacob continued

'You never know, the fighting might be over before I even arrive at the front! Let's hope I'm back by Christmas,' John-George told him as he gave his son a reassuring hug.

'But if we don't get going, I'll not make it at all,' John-George joked, hoping to ease the tension.

With a last minute rush, the whole family, including John-George's parents, finally set off to Newcastle. It was yet another day of incessant rain which did nothing to improve Maggie's feelings of impending gloom. On their arrival at the city's railway station, they were all shocked by the size of the crowd. There were vast numbers of men from every social class, indicative by their headgear, everything from the flat caps of the working man to the bowlers and straw boaters of the rich. Despite the seriousness of the situation, the general mood appeared quite buoyant. Maggie was struck by the way everyone seemed to be full of patriotic hysteria, with many waving flags and singing songs such as 'God save the King'. Some couples were laughing as they shared their last precious minutes with their loved one, some conversations seemed almost blasé, with no apparent thought that this might be the last one they ever had. Many parents appeared in good spirits as they proudly hovered around their young sons, saying their goodbyes.

John-George's mother was not one of them however; she was in more sombre mood. She hated the idea of her two sons having to go off to fight at the front. She'd already lost one son and certainly didn't want any harm to come to any one of her three surviving boys. James William had been a twin to John-George however he'd died soon after birth. Although it was thirty years previously, the feelings of loss had never fully left her.

Maggie was noticeably upset too, as she, along with the three children, said their last farewells. She pulled her husband close:

'Take care, my love,' she whispered in his ear, 'I love you and every day I'll be longing for your return.'

'I'll be back before you know it, now don't you be worrying lass!' he chided.

'Be good for your ma,' he ordered the children, 'You, especially,' he added, looking directly at his oldest son.

With a final wave and shouts of 'Good luck,' and 'Come back safe,' from everyone, the men boarded the train. Ann and Roland showed little emotion regarding their father's departure, being too young to realise its significance and even Jacob didn't realise that this might be the last time he saw his da. A single tear ran down his face but it was quickly removed with his sleeve, before anyone could spot it.

'Love ya da!' he cried as he spotted his father waving out of the carriage window.

On the journey home, Maggie tried to hold on to her husband's reassurance that he would soon be home again .She told herself to stay positive, especially when she realised his absence would have one benefit at least - no John-George around would mean no more babies for a while. She certainly didn't want any extra responsibility or additional problems to face whilst he was away.

Maggie returned to her house in Wylam Street with the other wives and mothers and tried to resume a normal everyday life but it wasn't easy. She eagerly awaited news but it was a long time coming. John-George had never been one for writing. He could read but he'd really never bothered at school with learning the rudiments of spellings or grammar, as he knew he was destined for the colliery.

When a letter finally arrived, in early December, it was extremely brief and uninformative. He was still training down south and not expecting to be sent abroad until the New Year .He told Maggie how much he was missing her and hoping that he would be home on leave before too long. Maggie found some comfort in his optimism but as Christmas approached and the weather turned, it was hard for her to remain positive. In addition, she was feeling extremely unwell and this made her long for John-George's return even more. It quickly dawned on her why she was feeling so tired and dispirited.

'You know what,' she confided to a friend, 'I'm sure I'm having another bairn! I must have got caught just before me husband left.'

'That ain't half bad luck Maggie, how will you cope?

'I'm just wondering that very thing me self,' Maggie replied. 'Me health's not too good and it's so hard when you're on your own.'

'How do you think John-George will take the news?' the friend continued.

'I don't want him to be any more concerned about me and the children, than I'm sure he is already. I know he'll worry whether I'll be able to manage. '

'Perhaps best not tell him then, until baby actually arrives,' the friend suggested.

Maggie considered this. Even though John-George had little interest in the process of childbirth, he was a caring father and he would be desperate to meet a new child, due, she guessed, in the late summer of 1915. Hopefully, she assured herself, he'd be home on leave before then or better still the war might just be over and then she'd tell him.

Maggie's hopes didn't materialise. The popular prediction that the war would be over by Christmas with the Germans successfully defeated had been proven to be wildly optimistic. They were proving to be a formidable enemy and rumours abounded that the government were trying to hide the truth about the vast number of British casualties. It was even said that the wounded were being shipped back at night to avoid the public's attention.

As the months moved past winter and into spring, all contact with John-George was lost. Maggie reckoned that by now, he must have been shipped to France to face life on the Western Front. But for her, indeed for most of those left behind, there was no inkling of what that involved. She was totally ignorant of the harsh realities of modern trench warfare, which was undoubtedly a good thing.

EIGHT
Northern France - 1915

It was mid-May before John-George finally left Britain. He found himself journeying, at nighttime, to Folkestone for his battalion's embarkation to Boulogne in France. Once on board the channel steamer, he and all his fellow soldiers were glad to be able to put down their equipment and sit on the open decks, whilst resting their heads on their bulging back packs. They were men with very different personalities but all appeared quietly confident. If they were feeling anxious none of them wanted to show it. Instead they enjoyed friendly, light-hearted chat with the usual extroverts making everyone laugh out loud with their jovial banter.

'Do you like my trousers?' one soldier joked as he sashayed up and down the deck, wiggling his torso, 'trouble is they're a bit tight around the armpits!'

The other men all sniggered, knowing exactly what he meant, as their compulsory khaki trousers did sit rather high up the body.

The itchy woollen underwear, consisting of a pair of long johns and a long sleeved vest, were an equal source of amusement especially as braces were required to go through loops on the non-elasticated underpants, to stop them falling down.

'Hope these don't snap,' commented one lad as he deliberately stretched both braces away from his chest, 'otherwise you might see more of me than you bargained for!'

As the evening progressed, conversation turned to life back home. It seemed many of the volunteers had similar backgrounds, with a significant number of them being miners from the Durham area.

'Well lads, there's no more days to be spent in pit for a while,' one young man remarked.

'Yeah, we'll all really miss our shifts, won't we!' laughed another as they began to share their individual stories.

John-George's mind was racing by the time he tried to have some rest in the early hours. Sleep didn't come easily - not only due to the impossible sleeping conditions - but also because of the mixed feelings he had about his current situation. There was a certain euphoria, knowing he was about to do his duty by serving King and country. Yet he had a heavy heart for he greatly missed

Maggie and his young family and wondered when, or worse still if, he would ever see them again. That was too unbearable to even contemplate.

Next morning there wasn't time to dwell on such things. First came a tedious journey by train to Cassel. The carriages were no better than cattle trucks and John-George and his fellow soldiers were hemmed in so tightly there was no room to move. There were constant stops and it took hours to arrive at the railhead. This was followed by an agonising, long march to billets at Volkerinckhove, a village in northern France.

'Why it's similar terrain to England,' John-George remarked to a comrade, as he travelled through the French countryside. The land was low lying and the landscape flat and fairly featureless apart from a few copses of trees and an occasional village.

'And the weather's the same too!' commented another, as the Flanders rain began to fall.

It seemed to John-George that the rain went on incessantly, causing the soil to turn into liquid mud. He was so glad of his heavy brown boots and his 'puttees' that were wound around his legs. These three-yard-long bandages supported his calves and gave added protection to the top of his boots, from the constant flow of water.

'It's enough having to carry all this equipment without having to contend with the uneven roads and the waterlogged ground,' a soldier complained as he watched one of his comrades fall down with exhaustion.

John-George agreed. There was the haversack on his back, which contained his much-needed personal items - cutlery, a shaving kit, one ground sheet and those invaluable spare pairs of socks. There was the all-important gas mask, hanging around his neck. He also had to carry the vital rifle and bayonet, a jack knife and an entrenching tool, in addition to pouches containing one hundred and fifty rounds of ammunition in a bandolier across his shoulder. Plus each man carried a mug and a mess tin, along with a canteen holding two pints of water.

John-George was also struggling with fatigue. No wonder I'm done in and my back's aching so much, he thought to himself as he trudged along. He was accustomed to hard discipline and back breaking work down the mine but having to walk so far, under such difficult conditions and carrying such excess weight was something he was just not used to. His initial enthusiasm was definitely waning and when he finally arrived at Dickebusch, a village five kilometres south west of Ypres, in early June, it did nothing to boost his morale. Billeted in tents, twelve men in each, his first night was filled with the constant sound of shellfire that limited sleep, despite his total exhaustion.

Very early the following morning, he was directed into some trenches and commanded to stand and wait until daylight, when he'd be given further instruction. He found out later this standing to attention, would happen every morning in case the Germans followed their usual custom of attacking before dawn. It was to be repeated, an hour before sunset, each day.

John-George spent the time looking around, surveying his surroundings and trying to peer through the half-light. He was struck by just how primitive the set up was and yet how cleverly it was created. The trenches, he knew from his training, were constructed over three lines. The first one, where he was now stood, was known as the front line because it was the first line of defence, facing the enemy.

He'd been told the front line in 1914 was nearly a thousand kilometres long from the coast of Belgium to the border of Switzerland. The British troops however only occupied just eighty miles of it, from near the town of Ypres in Belgium, to a position just south of the Somme in France.

The trench, John-George reckoned, was approximately six feet deep, not much taller than the tunnels he'd crawled in down the mine. The mud walls, slimy with moisture, were shored up by timber on each side. Along the top of the trench were rows of sandbags - for protection no doubt - plus an additional wall of barbed wire in front. Fire steps were built inside the front wall, allowing soldiers to stand on a ledge, to fire over the parapet at the enemy. The back of the trench was higher - again for added safety John-George concluded - so a soldier's head and shoulders were not silhouetted against the skyline.

He observed that the trenches weren't built in straight lines but seemed to follow a zig- zag pattern. It was only later that he realised the value of this layout. Not only did it provide a buffer, when a shell exploded inside the dugout, the arrangement also prevented the enemy firing along the full length of the trench, if or when they invaded.

John-George looked down at his feet, suddenly aware that they had lost all feeling despite his thick socks. No wonder! His boots were virtually submerged in the thick, rancid-smelling mud, almost a foot deep, despite the presence of duckboards along the ground. He looked around and noticed his fellow soldiers were plastered in mud, even their faces were caked in it.

His thoughts quickly turned to his own personal needs: Where and how would he clean himself and dry his sodden clothes?

How was he going to be able to sleep in such conditions? Where would he go to the toilet and how would he eat and drink without succumbing to illness? This was not what he had expected at all and a sick feeling began to envelop him.

Suddenly he was aware of his sergeant calling him to arms:
'Stand to!' a deep voice commanded.

He immediately jumped to attention. Then came a further order to 'fix bayonets' and have his rifle inspected. The sergeant came to check that none of the soldiers were exposing their heads to enemy snipers and warned them that the greatest danger from attack would always be at dawn and dusk. Finally, John-George and his comrades were provided with some welcome food - cold bacon, bread and jam but were told the communication trenches, that ran between the front and reserve line, were so water logged, many of the rations had failed to arrive. This news did nothing to boost his morale.

The next day, despite having had barely three hours of very uncomfortable sleep John-George experienced his first proper turn in the firing line. He was ordered to stand facing the enemy, across a narrow strip of land, between opposing trenches, the area referred to as 'No Man's Land.' It consisted of a desolate area of ground, no more than a hundred foot wide, filled with deep puddles and thick mud which John-George knew they would have to cross, if the command came to go 'over the top' to launch an attack.

He didn't have to wait long. The order was given and the first line of soldiers ventured through the gaps in the parapets - known as sally ports - with great trepidation. John-George advanced, with every instinct in his body telling him to try and escape being a sitting target. As soon as possible, he threw himself into the first available crater.

From there he tried to shoot any German soldier whose head appeared out of the enemy trenches, as he had been trained to do. But as shells exploded overhead and the gunfire increased, the sounds of the wounded and the dying crying out for help were tortuous to hear. To John-George, seeing bleeding bodies and shattered limbs seemed nothing more than senseless murder.

It felt like an eternity before the heavy bombardment ceased.

John-George was immensely relieved when the attack was finally over and an order was given to retreat. He was totally exhausted as he dived back through the sally port. He was further instructed to grab something to eat before a possible counter attack. The soldiers helped one another to unhook their mess tins from their backs and enjoyed their first hot meal and drink, given to them by the quartermaster.

'I've never known stew taste this good,' one of them remarked and they all agreed, as they sat, their backs against the reinforced walls, with just a candle to give them light.

It was traumatic for most of the men that day, for many it was their first experience of death on such a scale. Most of them felt a sense of guilt that they were still alive and able to eat a hearty meal, especially when news filtered through, of fifty casualties in total, within the tenth battalion. John-George was both appalled and disillusioned. He'd quite enjoyed the tough training with its early morning runs, rifle drill, square bashing and bayonet practice. But now the reality of war was stark and terrifying and not at all what he had envisaged.

He learnt that many of the battalion had died simply because they had forgotten to keep their heads down in the parapets even before they set off. Others had been mortally wounded in no man's land by snipers or shellfire and one had simply lost his life as a result of a careless ally firing at him by mistake.

That evening, no one was willing to talk about the losses - it was too raw and too close for comfort to even contemplate. John-George was particularly distressed when he learnt one of those killed was a Bowburn lad.

Some respite came at the end of the week, when they were removed from the front line and placed behind in a support line which held extra troops and supplies ready to be pushed forward in case of an attack. John-George was glad to be out of the main action for a while but he was becoming acutely aware of the awful living conditions within the trenches. Body lice and rats were everywhere, plaguing the soldiers day and night.

'A rat, as big as a cat, woke me with a start last night, as its tail swished across me face,' a soldier complained to John-George one morning.

'Yeah! Looks like a bloody rat has been at our food rations,' John-George replied angrily as he spotted some half-eaten bread.

Worse still, they regularly witnessed the same wretched vermin gorging on the human flesh that lay rotting around them. Eating it, made the rats' faces swell and whiten visibly, so much so, they were virtually luminous in the darkness at the bottom of the trench.

'I reckon I'm going to volunteer for rat catching duty,' John-George remarked, 'it'll give me great pleasure to kill the blighters! I'm going to put a small piece of cheese on the end of my bayonet, wait for the rat to have a nibble and then pull the trigger!'

This suggestion was loved by all.

There was also the added problem of the equally annoying

lice, which crawled over their filthy clothes. The soldiers watched as the hungry, transparent bodies of the lice turned black after sucking their fill of the men's blood.

'Those lice are crawling in me clothes, what's a man to do?' a young soldier cried in torment.

'Turn your vest inside out,' another suggested.

'No, best thing to do is run a lighted match along the seam of your trousers,' one sufferer advised.

Blue bottles and cockroaches added to the misery and the appalling conditions meant many of the men were prone to illnesses such as dysentery and trench fever. It made John-George reluctant to use the latrines, plus the fact there was no privacy.

After another week, he was relieved when orders were given to retreat, further back still, to the reserve line, whose function was to move forward quite quickly, but only in an emergency. He soon discovered this trench had its own drawbacks. The days seemed endless and boredom was a real problem. The only relief was the bacon sandwich and shot of rum, which became a welcome part of the daily routine.

A further week on, John-George found himself posted to a billet near Vlamertinghe, in Belgium. This provided a very welcome two weeks of rest. Although 'rest' was a relative term, there was nearly always something for the soldiers to do, such as labouring and carrying or a series of training exercises and inspections. John-George didn't really mind such activities although he preferred it when there were opportunities to relax - when he could play sport and contact family back home.

When it came to writing letters, John-George felt aggrieved that he wasn't more literate and wished he'd paid more attention in school. How he longed to be able to express his deep sadness at being away from Maggie and to convey how much he missed her and the children. He was only able to script a simple note and hoped she would be happy just to hear from him. As yet, he was still waiting to receive news from her and could hardly bear it when his comrades showed him their love letters and, for some, their parcels - containing such delights as clean socks, bars of chocolate, tobacco and other treats.

He was certainly totally unaware that dramatic events were unfolding back home…

Maggie was finding life as a single parent an immense struggle. She was now thinking that the mining company's weekly offering of seven shillings was small and inadequate compensation for John-George's absence. There was additional government help with the separation allowance - a total of twelve shillings and sixpence a week, plus an extra two and six for each child. But the money never seemed to stretch far enough and every week there was a decision to be made on what was the most urgent need and what would have to wait.

Looking after the children was demanding, particularly Jacob, as his behaviour had deteriorated since his father's departure. He badgered Maggie endlessly.

'When's da coming back home?' was his constant question.

'Soon, I'm sure it will be very soon,' she would answer every time, knowing full well it was an empty promise.

'You always say that!' Jacob would reply impatiently, 'but it never happens.'

By the summer of 1915, even Maggie was feeling increasingly frustrated by the lack of news. Her confinement was looming and she desperately hoped - prayed even - that her husband would return. Even if the war wasn't over, she hoped he might be able to obtain leave so that he could meet his new child when it arrived. Yet she had no idea of either his whereabouts or the circumstances in which he found himself. She was ignorant of the rule that no soldier could disclose their location and that all letters had to be censored to ensure this instruction was enforced.

When some news regarding the front line finally reached her, it certainly wasn't the communiqué she'd been hoping for.

'I hear Bowburn's had its first casualty,' one of the neighbours informed her, 'It's Christopher Walker Carling from Crowtrees Cottage. He was killed on the last day of July apparently. Imagine, dead at just twenty- three.'

'It's his poor mother I feel sorry for,' Maggie replied, 'I'm just glad I don't know her personally.'

'There's going to be a memorial service for him at the church next week, if you want to pay your respects. He was in the tenth battalion of the Durham Light Infantry, isn't that the company whom your husband is with?'

Maggie could barely answer on hearing mention of the tenth battalion. She simply patted her stomach, 'It depends on when the bairn arrives whether I get to the service,' was all she said before walking on.

This news had stunned her, it made the war so much more of a reality, knowing that someone in John-George's actual battalion was one of the casualties. She became more anxious than ever. Never had she ached so much for John-George and longed for him to come home. She gave way to self-pitying tears and feared for the child within her.

Just twelve days later she went into labour, with her dearest wish unfulfilled. After several hours, with just the help of the local midwife, Maggie gave birth to a third boy.

The children were excited to see their new brother and Ann, particularly, fussed over him.

'What are we going to call him?' Ann was eager to know.

'Well I've been giving it lots of thought and I think I've had a good idea. How about we name him John-George, after his da?'

'I like that,' Ann replied.

'Yes and I think he looks like your da too,' Maggie responded.

'No! He doesn't!' Jacob remarked, rather annoyed, 'can't you see he's got my hair colouring, same as you, ma.' Secretly, Jacob felt some resentment to the child, knowing he would bring added work and responsibility, some of which would fall on him. Nor did he want the child to be named after his father. At the moment, he felt he was the one who was closest to his da and he didn't want that to alter, when his da returned.

'I like the name Tommy,' Jacob suggested instead. He knew it was the nickname given to all the British soldiers and felt it would be quite appropriate. None of the family agreed.

The following day, Maggie realised that John-George needed to be informed by letter that she had given birth to their fourth child. She accepted that there would be a delay before this news would reach him or even the possibility that he might never hear - but she was determined to try. News that he had a son - born on August 12th, 1915 and named John-George in honour of him - would undoubtedly be a great shock but a good one, she hoped, at least.

NINE
Belgium - 1915

In September 1915, John-George and his comrades in the tenth battalion found themselves being moved by train towards Ypres. As they were travelling along, they were suddenly aware of a great explosion further down the line. The Germans had shelled their open trucks causing enormous devastation. The train came to an immediate halt and all the uninjured men made their way out into the open. John-George was horrified by the extent of the destruction and even more distraught, when the commanding officer informed them later,

'We've lost forty men and several are so badly injured they won't see action again.'

The great anger they all felt, on hearing this, made them even more determined to fight on. Yet there seemed to be a state of stalemate, with neither side able to make any great progress. John-George was starting to realise this war was not going to be resolved in a hurry and although he was as keen as the rest to beat the Huns, he was beginning to question just how much longer he could stay focused.

Life in the trenches was becoming increasingly unbearable. The weather was deteriorating and all the soldiers found that their feet were now almost permanently under water. John-George's feet, like many of his fellow soldiers, had swollen to nearly twice their normal size and he could barely feel his toes most of the time.

'You've contracted a fungal infection, known as trench foot,' one of the medical officers informed him.

'The best remedy is to dry your feet and change your socks two or three times a day.'

'I'm going to have to write then to me missus' and ask her to send me half a dozen pairs of extra-large socks,' John-George remarked and then laughed as he added, 'then me feet might stay dry for half a day at least!'

It was hardly a joke but staying positive seemed to be only way to cope.

'Yeah, but it'll not stop them wretched rats from biting your toes when you're asleep!' his mate Allan, retorted. 'Nor the bleeding lice which seem to get everywhere!'

'The smell of the whale oil might just deter them!' someone

else suggested, referring to one of the prescribed remedies for trench foot.

All the men tried to make light of it but in truth the situation was grim. Some of the men developed gangrene, which meant they had to have their infected toes removed. John-George feared this might happen to him but he tried not to think about it.

There were other on-going problems. The lack of overhead cover meant all the infantry were exposed to the elements and the regulation army blankets offered scant protection from the bitter cold. It was evident some men were suffering from exposure and frost bite.

'I actually appreciate me long johns and itchy woollen socks now,' John-George remarked as he was allocated to a two hour sentry duty.

'Yes, but the cold does have one plus side - it keeps you awake!' his friend reminded him.

It was vital to stay awake because as one unfortunate soldier had learnt to his cost, under military law, the penalty for sleeping on guard was the firing squad.

Part of his duty involved sitting in a 'sap'- an appendage that went out from the front line into No man's land. It was used as a listening post to gain information from the German line. This night, John-George heard nothing and he struggled with the intense cold, as he had to remain stationary.

'I reckon it's almost as bad as last year, when we had the coldest winter in living memory,' his relief man complained and John-George's frozen body told him that he agreed.

Just after midnight, he was given permission to make a very welcome brew. After digging a small hole in the side of the trench, he lit a fire and boiled some water in his mess tin. He then added some tealeaves and condensed milk. It might not have tasted the best tea ever but it was warm and comforting.

Overhead was a constant noise of artillery shell fire, which seemed like a colossal roar, but for a few moments, he was able to forget it and think instead of home. Tomorrow marked the end of duty and a return to the billet. Maybe, John-George reflected, just maybe, there'd be some much-needed news of home awaiting him...

* * * * *

'I've a son, a new son,' John-George called out to anyone who would listen. He held his arms aloft with the letter in his hand. He noted that the letter was posted back in late August.

At first he couldn't take in the news that Maggie had given birth in his absence and made him a father again for the fourth time.

'I didn't even know she was in the family way,' he explained to his bemused comrades.

'That's great news though, isn't it,' his friend remarked, giving him a congratulatory slap on the back.

'Are you sure it's your child though? ' another soldier suggested unkindly, puzzled by the fact that John-George didn't know.

John-George was taken aback for a moment. He had never once doubted his wife's fidelity and hadn't even considered that possibility.

'Well she's calling him John-George, after me,' he retaliated, feeling that fact alone was proof of his son's paternity, not that he needed any.

'Can someone help me send a decent note back to me wife, telling her how happy I am?' he asked hopefully and was delighted when there were several willing volunteers all happy to relay good tidings for once.

For the next few days, his spirits were lifted. It had been a surprise hearing of his fourth child and he viewed it with mixed emotions but it was good to have news of a birth when faced with so much death. He couldn't wait to meet him. He was hopeful that leave would be granted in the near future, knowing that it was every soldier's entitlement, after a year of service. But now he longed more than ever for the war to be over, so that he could return home for good. He began to dread the day when the rota demanded he was back in the front line, fearing most the signal to 'go over the top' to cross No man's land and attack the German trenches, in case the unthinkable happened.

He was scared, petrified even, although he wasn't going to admit it to anyone. He was convinced that others felt exactly the same.

Until he'd come to war, he hadn't seen many corpses before, except when there'd been an occasional tragic accident at the pit. Now dead bodies were an everyday occurrence. He could be talking to a fellow soldier in the trenches one minute and the next moment, he'd witness his comrade suddenly drop down dead, with a single sniper's bullet to the head. Worse still, the bodies sometimes stayed where they fell for hours, before they could be transported into the support trench. The stench, from the rotting corpses, in No man's land, was equally repugnant to him. It completely pervaded the atmosphere. Many tried to block the odour, by smoking strong Turkish cigarettes, with a powerful scent, but John-George couldn't get used to them.

Other comrades had been mown down in No Man's land and

had simply been swallowed up, in the liquid mud and even trampled on. Screams of wounded men, who were beyond rescue, haunted John-George's mind. Many who were rescued, were barely alive. He came across one of his friends whose leg had been blown off. The shrapnel wound had torn it into pieces.

'Don't leave me,' his comrade begged. John-George knelt beside him, feeling powerless to help, so simply took hold of his hand. 'Mother!' the man cried as he took his final breath. John-George felt relief that death had come swiftly and the soldier's suffering was over. But it left him traumatised and those final images haunted him for weeks to come.

To him the squalor of the trenches and the waste of human life was abhorrent. He knew for certain that he'd never have volunteered, if he'd had half of an idea of what the reality was going to be. He could fully appreciate why those 'conchies' had refused to fight - the futility of it all was immeasurable. He felt guilty at how desensitised he'd become by the loss of his comrades but it was the only way he could cope with the appalling devastation and vast numbers of casualties that he encountered.

Worst of all, despite their best efforts and the unremitting list of losses, no decisive breakthrough was being achieved. There had still been no major battles and it was becoming a war of attrition- a question of which side could outlast the other with regard to both men and supplies. At that moment in time John-George had no idea of the answer. The only thing he was sure about was that his sense of patriotism was fading and he was fearful of never returning home to Blighty. Every day he was convinced that it would be his time to die.

'Whose turn next?' was on everyone's lips.

TEN
Bowburn - 1915/1916

Maggie was also questioning the validity of this on-going war as she continued to find life an uphill struggle. The demands of a new baby wore her down as she tried to cope with sleep deprivation. The baby was constantly fretful and her initial joy at his arrival was tinged with regret that she'd had another child. She was also disheartened that almost every week someone in the village was telling her of yet another casualty from the local area.

In October, it was the manager of Bowburn colliery who received bad news. Mr Harle learnt that his son William had been wounded in the neck by shrapnel and was in hospital in Boulogne. There was some consolation; the latest report stated, he was holding on to life, so Maggie truly hoped he'd manage to pull through.

Her spirits were raised a little in November, when the Bowburn authorities announced there was to be a concert at the council school. It was a fund raising venture with the intention of providing Christmas presents for any serving soldier or sailor who'd worked at Bowburn colliery. Maggie decided to attend - the idea that John-George might be sent a present appealed to her. She felt it more likely he would receive something on the front line, if it was sent through official channels and that certainty brought her some comfort.

Just the thought of Christmas and all the problems it would bring, was starting to bother Maggie. There was no money to spare for presents and certainly any purchase of luxury food was out of the question. She was also brooding on the fact that she would have to spend a second Christmas alone with the children.

It began to lead Maggie into a downward spiral of depression, which continued throughout the long winter months and into the spring of 1916. Maggie couldn't accept that the war seemed to be in a state of complete deadlock and her mood was black, most days. Ultimately this had a negative impact on the children.

They frequently complained because they were hungry and their health began to suffer as a result of their poor diet. Roland's asthma was always at its worst at this time of year but buying medicine was not an option. She'd been informed that he really needed a tincture of belladonna, which was known to be well tolerated by children but she just couldn't afford it.

Maggie chose not to send the two oldest children to school regularly, even though it was literally across the road and despite the fact that it was compulsory for all those between the age of five and ten. The truth was she couldn't be bothered - besides she had an excuse - she didn't have the means to clothe them properly. Jacob always seemed to need new boots and his clothes couldn't realistically be passed on to Ann, so kitting her out was always more of a financial burden than providing for the two youngest boys.

No schooling though created boredom, particularly for Jacob who was increasingly reluctant to help Maggie with chores. Animosity grew between them as Maggie deemed him to be nothing but trouble.

'Get out of my sight, I don't want you around anymore!' Maggie screamed one day in exasperation as Jacob continuously taunted his younger siblings. Even Ann, who normally wasn't any bother, had retaliated and hit her brother in frustration.

Whereas normally he would disappear for an hour or two, this time Jacob took his mother at her word. Darkness descended and there was no sign of him. When he finally turned up next morning, Maggie was beside herself, for in truth, she had been very worried about him. She genuinely loved him and didn't wish him to come to any harm. Equally she knew Jacob loved her in return, even though he was at the age when he didn't want to admit it. But at the same time she was angry that he'd put her through such anxiety. She swore at him in frustration and demanded to know what he'd been up to.

'I just kipped down at me friend's house, on the floor,' he retorted, 'you told me to go, so I did!'

Maggie knew her relationship with Jacob was deteriorating but she felt powerless to stop its decline. She knew his da would have disciplined him and Jacob wouldn't have dared to disobey but he just didn't take any notice of her. She felt quite overwhelmed with everything and realised she was barely coping. She'd lost regular contact with her sisters, as they were now married with their own children and Jacob and Marian never got in touch.

Occasionally she saw her parents-in-law, as they still lived in a house just further up from hers, which she appreciated. It only needed Maggie to say,

'Let's go see grandma and granddad,' and the children would be ready in no time, knowing it meant they'd be guaranteed better meals than those their mother would give them. But more often than not, Maggie couldn't face the effort involved.

Maggie tended to rely on a good friend down the street called Jenny Bell, who lived at number twenty. She had three children of similar age and both their families enjoyed playing out on the street together. Whenever the two women met up, they would chat freely and console each other on how hard life was without their husband's support. But then Maggie heard news in March that Jenny's husband Robert had been killed. She felt guilty but she couldn't bear to contact her. It wasn't that she was indifferent, she just didn't want to face up to realities. Would it be John-George next on the casualty list? If she didn't think about it, perhaps, she told herself, it might never happen.

The following weeks went by as usual with still no letter from John-George and Maggie found it impossible not to worry but she tried to put it to the back of her mind. She took to retiring early, as sleep brought release from her anxieties, plus there seemed to be no point in staying up, when there was no one to chat to, after the children had gone down for the night.

She was just completing her final chores one evening and making sure the baby was settled, when she heard a faint knocking on the front door. Who could that be, she asked herself, at such a late hour? She decided not to answer at first but then the caller knocked again, louder this time.

She opened the door rather tentatively and peered into the darkness, seeing the outline of a man dressed in uniform and carrying a suitcase. A voice she knew broke the silence,

'Maggie, it's me, don't you recognise me!'

She looked the man up and down, hardly able to believe it was her husband…

'Is it you, is it really you, John-George?' she uttered incredulously.

With that, she rushed forward and threw her arms around him, holding him tightly, never wanting to let go.

It wasn't until they got inside that John-George reacted; overcome with emotion, he began to cry. The anticipation had been so great and yet the journey and now the reality of being back home seemed so strange and such a stark contrast to life at the front.

'Why didn't you tell me you were coming?' Maggie asked as she gently wiped away the tears that were trickling down his face.

'We were given hardly a day's notice,' he explained, 'and I was fearful that it might be cancelled at the last minute… if there was a sudden attack.'

'I never imagined it could be you,' Maggie replied, still in shock, but then her thoughts turned to her family upstairs.

'Why, I must go and wake the children,' she suggested.

She moved towards the stairs but John-George grabbed her arm, 'Leave them be Maggie,' he said, 'best not disturb them.'

With that, he removed the kitbag from his aching back, took off his thick, khaki coat and his heavy boots, placed his roll of bedding and suitcase against the wall and carefully laid his rifle down on the floor. His mind tried to focus on his surroundings - he looked around, attempting to familiarise himself with the layout, and then he spotted his favourite armchair. As he went to sit down, he became aware of a slight whimper, coming from the opposite corner of the room. He turned towards the noise and reacted instantly.

'Oh! Let me see, let me see,' he said almost pushing past his wife, attempting to hide his embarrassment. How could he have forgotten to ask about his new son when so many of his recent thoughts had been centred on little John-George? He bent down and gently picked up the stirring child, cradling him in his arms. This was harder for him than he had ever imagined. He had dreamt of this reunion for what had seemed an eternity, but the adjustments he had to make, were proving very difficult. He was aware this child was his, yet he didn't know him. The reality was not easy to come to terms with, plus he couldn't bear to think that he would have to leave him again, in just seven days… He held him close and sobbed bitterly. Maggie tried to console her husband but it all proved too much and she began to weep as well. They put the baby down and held each other tightly, without speaking a word.

Suddenly, an unexpected sound behind them startled the pair. It was Jacob. He had been disturbed and was now charging down the stairs. The loud noise made John-George flinch; for a moment he imagined he was back in the trenches. He froze and when Jacob, so overcome with joy, jumped on him, he recoiled as if under attack.

'You don't ever have to go back, da, do you?' Jacob enquired, having no idea of the insensitivity of this question.

'I'll be home for about a week,' his da replied and then, trying to regain his composure, added, 'but let's not think about it.'

Maggie stared hard at her husband. His face seemed much thinner and she was struck by the greyness of his colouring. The sparkle in his eyes had gone and she could see he'd lost weight.

'Do you want something to eat?' she asked concerned, but he shook his head. He wasn't used to eating at this time of the evening, besides he had no appetite.

After a brief conversation, John-George suddenly

announced,

'I'm done in Maggie, do you mind if I go to bed?'

'That's ok, I think it's time we all retired,' Maggie answered and turning to Jacob she promised, 'We'll catch up with da in the morning.'

Jacob had other ideas - he had discovered his father's rifle and was examining it carefully. He was shocked by its weight but was enjoying the pretence of pulling the trigger repeatedly, allowing his imagination to wander.

'Come on! Back to bed!' his mother ordered sharply and don't you go disturbing your brother and sister,' she added impatiently. She half expected him to ignore her but this time, wanting to please his da, he willingly complied.

That night, John-George lay side by side with his wife but his mind was unsettled and wandered back to France. He could hear the voices of his officers and the noises of war in his head and they troubled him immensely Maggie reached out to hold him but he didn't respond in the way she'd hoped. She so wanted him to caress her tenderly, in the way he used to.

'It's wonderful to have you home,' she whispered, drawing up close, enjoying the warmth of his body. It was then that she realised he was shaking.

'Try to go to sleep,' she told him, telling herself to be patient. She'd waited so long to be reunited; she could certainly wait another day for intimacy.

The following morning, Ann and Roland were overwhelmed when they found out their father was asleep upstairs. Although they could barely remember him and certainly had little concept of war or what 'leave' actually meant, they were still excited, knowing that something special was happening. They were already in playful mood, having discovered their da's belongings and were now pretending to be soldiers. Roland had picked up his father's puttees and was attempting to wind them in coils around both of his legs. He was encouraging Ann to join in and there were shrieks of laughter as the bandages rendered him incapable of walking, so he jumped around the room, with bunny hops.

John-George came down to join them later that morning and Maggie was keen to encourage him to eat. He was subdued but anxious to try and enjoy his family and make their acquaintance. He was surprised by how much the children had changed over the last eighteen months.

'I barely recognise them,' he told Maggie, as all three children chatted away to him.

Maggie didn't reply; she was thinking that her husband had

changed too but she didn't want to express such feelings out loud. He seemed exhausted. Understandably, he was reluctant to speak of anything regarding the war, but Maggie was more upset that he didn't seem very willing to initiate any conversation at all.

'I think I better go and call on my folks,' he announced, as the family were just beginning to relax.

'Will you be back for your dinner?' Maggie enquired but John-George had gone before she finished the sentence. She doubted if he'd even heard her.

He returned a few hours later but spoke little of the reaction of his parents or what had been discussed. That evening when they were alone, Maggie tried to ask him more. All he would tell her was how hard he was finding it. Having uninhibited freedom was so strange and unfamiliar to him and he explained that he had a real sense of guilt, thinking of his mates back in France.

Maggie tried to be patient but she could foresee the week passing, without her being able to share any of the problems she'd had to face during his absence. She felt it wouldn't be fair to tell him of her depression or the difficulties she was having with Jacob. He certainly didn't seem to have the stamina to discipline their eldest son and showed no willingness to talk about money issues and their daily struggles. Even affection was limited to an occasional hug, although Maggie was determined to show him how much she loved and needed him.

Gradually as time passed, John-George became less edgy: he began to play more with the children and enjoyed getting to know the baby. He even apologised to Maggie for being so quiet and reassured her that he still loved her deeply. She encouraged him constantly and was pleased when he was finally able to be intimate, although their union was over quickly and was not nearly as satisfying as what she remembered.

When the last day of his leave arrived, John-George was once again reduced to tears.

'Be good for your ma,' he ordered Ann and Roland, fighting to regain his composure. Then turning to Jacob, he placed his hand firmly on the boy's shoulder and tried to speak sternly, 'You have to be the man of the house whilst I'm away, so make sure you always do as your ma asks.'

Jacob nodded but his eyes averted his mother's gaze.

Finally, John-George turned to Maggie, 'Don't you be fretting after I've gone. Remember I love you always,' he said softly as his voice began to break. 'If I don't come back, Maggie, promise me that you'll be brave. I'd like you to be happy and marry…'

Maggie put her finger to his lips and stopped him before he could complete what he wanted to say.

'Don't think of such things,' she said as she began weeping uncontrollably.

John-George wrapped his arms lovingly around his wife and kissed her tenderly on the cheek. Then he hugged each child in turn.

He'd already insisted that Maggie and the children didn't escort him to the railway station, feeling that their parting would be too painful. Instead, they stood outside their home and watched in silence, as he walked off down the street until he'd disappeared round the corner. Maggie felt this parting was worse, far worse than the first one and that had been difficult enough. How she had longed for him to return, yet it was over so soon and it had not been the wonderful re-union that she had expected it to be. She was filled with utter despondency and the children were more subdued than usual, especially Jacob. A sense of gloom pervaded the house for the rest of that day and in the days that followed.

John-George himself was mortified. He had no desire to return to face what he thought was the inevitable. On his journey back, he punished himself with feelings of guilt - he recognised that he had appeared distant and troubled while at home when this was not what he had intended. Why was that? He didn't truly know the answer. But one thing he did know, he had an awful premonition that he would never see his family again.

* * * * *

Maggie continued to struggle with her morbid thoughts on a daily basis. She needed to confide in someone but there was no one to turn to. The children, especially Jacob, had seemed very unsettled since their father's departure and Maggie herself was feeling increasingly guilty. Had other wives, she wondered, found their husband's time of leave to be a disappointment, or was it just her experience? It wasn't really something you could discuss with the neighbours. She hadn't had a chance to see her in-laws to ask them how they felt about their son. Had he appeared distant to them, too? She must, she promised herself, make the effort to go and visit them and soon.

However, before the opportunity arose to carry out these intentions, her plans were thwarted. It was mid-morning, on a warm July day, when Maggie was startled by a loud knock on her door. It had an urgency, which suggested she was needed at once. Rushing to open it, she almost tripped over her youngest child, as he crawled on the stone floor. Maggie swore under her breath and pulled open the door impatiently.

On the verge of shouting, 'What do you want?' she stopped herself when she realised it was actually her mother-in-law who had come to visit. Maggie noticed her ashen appearance and realised she had been crying. It was obvious something was amiss.

Silent at first, Ann was holding her arm aloft, frantically waving a piece of paper in the air.

'Maggie, Maggie it's our Henry - he's been killed,' she finally blurted out and then with head bowed, she began sobbing uncontrollably.

Maggie read the letter for herself. The words took a while to sink in. 'painful duty to inform you… Henry Purvis… killed on July 10th 1916...'

She knew exactly what this loss would mean to Ann. She was so proud of her Henry, achieving his position of lance sergeant when they were just simple folk with no proper education and no standing in society. It would simply destroy her. However, Maggie had absolutely no energy with which to comfort her.

'I'm so sorry, Ann,' was all that she could bring herself to utter. Then seeing what a state she was in, she quickly added, 'Come on let me take you back home to John.'

She gently took hold of her mother-in-law's arm to provide support, she was so overcome with grief that her frail body was in a virtual state of collapse.

Maggie realised she too was shaking, as she walked back home. Even though such news was half expected, the shock was still immense. It was just so unbearable. Where and when was the pain and agony of this war going to end? She felt like shutting herself away in the house, so she never had to face anything so awful ever again…

ELEVEN
Arras, France - 1916

Fortunately John-George wasn't aware of his brother's tragic death. He had been moved, nearer to the town of Arras in France, in readiness for the forthcoming battle of the Somme. Throughout August 1916, he found himself entrenched near Longeville village, trying to capture Denville Wood. Eventually his battalion had some success, capturing sixty German prisoners but John-George and his comrades all questioned if it was worth the great cost. For it left the battalion seriously weakened, with a total of three hundred and eighty-one men, either killed, wounded or missing, including their commanding officer Colonel H Morant.

It seemed success came at too great a price, 'I think we were fools to rush into the infantry,' John-George remarked after the latest venture into enemy territory, 'we are the only people who have to go into no man's land and make attacks.'

'Yes perhaps if we hadn't been so quick to enlist, I might have joined the Army Services Corp, especially as they earn more money than us,' his friend Allan replied.

All the men were becoming demoralised. Despite their tremendous efforts, little progress was being achieved. For some of his comrades, it all became too much. John-George was horrified as he witnessed friends suffering mental breakdown which rendered them incapable of service and even led a few to desert their posts. He knew this was punishable by execution but he didn't want to even think about that, as he observed them being led away. Other soldiers suffered such severe shell shock and were affected so badly, he learnt they were to be transported back home.

'I reckon some of them will face a future life in an asylum,' one of the officers remarked, without a thought for the negative effect it would have on his men.

Those still fit for action were greatly relieved when a few days later, instructions were given for them to be bussed to the town of Arras, for a period of recreation.

John-George was able during this time to send a brief letter home. He knew it would be censored so he didn't write anything of his whereabouts or disclose the outcome of any of the battles.

He particularly wanted to tell his wife Maggie how much he was missing her. He was fully aware that he'd failed her somewhat on his visit home and hadn't been quite the man she deserved but he attributed this to stress. It certainly didn't mean he had lost his desire for her. In fact, every night as he endeavoured to sleep, his thoughts turned to her. He ached for her physically and longed to have the opportunity to be back with her once more, hoping to make amends. But this was not something to write home about. He would keep his frustrations to himself.

He had witnessed some of his comrades going off with French women who offered to 'service' them for a fee of anything between two and eight shillings. But he had no wish to be with another woman - besides he'd heard how many of the men were succumbing to venereal disease.

Nor did he want to upset Maggie, by telling her that life on the front, with all its brutality, was becoming more like 'hell on earth' every day. He knew how much she looked forward to hearing from him and that she needed encouragement and hope rather than negativity and despair.

So instead he simply copied a fairly standard letter:

Just been told we are moving to 'A destination unknown'. You may not hear from me again for a while but do not worry. Can't wait to see you all again.

Love you always.

John-George.

In a desperate attempt to break the deadlock, John-George was aware that some of the British troops were now being moved underground, so they could dig tunnels to plant mines under the German trenches. Would this finally lead to a successful conclusion, he wondered, although he doubted it, convinced they were in for a long haul. He and his comrades in the tenth battalion were stationed at the Wancourt line, where the weather was worsening by the day and thick snow began to fall, as winter approached. Not only were conditions under foot at their worst, the Germans had just unleashed their deadliest new weapon – poison gas attacks. It was so lethal, all the men came to fear it, more than any other weapon.

'It's a silent, deadly killer,' the soldiers were warned by their commanding officer, 'and in case of attack, you must put on your gas mask immediately.'

It wasn't long before John-George understood the word 'immediately' as he witnessed the appalling effects for himself. He'd managed to secure his mask in time but a few of his fellow soldiers weren't so fortunate and left it too late. At first, there were no apparent ill effects but then they complained of an intense pain, as their bodies were gripped by nausea and vomiting. Red spots appeared on their skin, which quickly turned to painful blisters, caused by the chemical burn and in severe cases they were fatal. It was unbearable to watch as some soldiers slowly succumbed to an agonising death.

For John-George it seemed as if he was existing in a valley of death. When would the torture ever end? Every day he woke up certain that it would be his last. And yet he was almost wishing for instant death, a sniper's bullet would be best, at least that would bring an end to his daily nightmare. It was far more palatable than the prospect of permanent disfigurement or a slow, lingering death from horrendous wounds or the dreaded inhalation of the insidious mustard gas.

Bowburn…

Maggie was so relieved when she received John-George's letter in the Autumn of 1916. At least she knew he had survived, for now at least. She shared the good news with the children but Jacob didn't see it like that.

'Going to a destination unknown,' he repeated, ' that means he's not coming back here then.'

'Not yet,' Maggie agreed, 'but hopefully he'll be granted more leave in the near future.'

'That's not the news I want to hear,' he said bitterly.

As time passed, Jacob had grown more understanding about the war and its consequences.

He'd heard that the man who'd created the new volunteer army - Lord Kitchener - had drowned on the cruiser H.M.S. Hampshire when it was torpedoed, along with everyone on board. That had shocked him.

He'd been told that the German Kaiser referred to some of the British troops as a 'Contemptible little army.' That had really infuriated him, recognising it as an insult, especially when it came from the man who was actually the grandson of Queen Victoria.

He'd heard about the 'Big Push', where everyone was hopeful that the Germans were going to be finally beaten, in a new campaign at the Somme. This had heartened him, although he was scared to think that might be the place where his da had been sent.

He felt proud of his da and wanted to emulate him. He made up his mind that when he was old enough, he would become a soldier in the army and better still, he would join the Durham Light Infantry. He decided not to share this idea with his mother, realising it wouldn't go down too well. Besides, he was fully aware that his mother was totally preoccupied with her own worries and had little time for him.

Maggie's emotions were certainly fragile and she veered from positivity to total misery. She too had heard about the Big Push and wondered if she dare feel optimistic that the war may just be coming to an end. But the negative feelings soon returned as she heard of the awful casualty figures. She couldn't comprehend it, when told the allies had lost twenty thousand men, on one single day, at the start of the battle of the Somme.

Even more alarming was the government's attempt to rally people to get behind the war effort by releasing a movie entitled, 'The Battle of the Somme.' Maggie, along with millions of others in Britain, went to see the film and was distraught by what she witnessed. To see first-hand the grotesque images of men dying in horrific ways, she found truly horrendous.

The film became the topic of conversation on everyone's lips, creating a wave of sympathy for all the casualties and a great sense of pride for what they'd sacrificed.

'You know we're lost more Bowburn men this year, than in 1914 and 1915 put together,' one of the locals informed Maggie, 'the fight must continue, otherwise their sacrifice is in vain.'

Maggie disagreed. She was appalled by the losses. She thought back to William Blenkinsop, who'd died on the Somme in August. Not only had his younger brother Richard been killed, just two months previously, but also she recalled that he was in the same battalion as her husband. Once more, this was becoming far too close to home for comfort.

Maggie couldn't bring herself to call on Mrs Blenkinsop. She felt she ought to, but what could she say? She was still reeling from these deaths, when she learnt of yet more bad news for the village's inhabitants. In September, another Bowburn lad - and member of the tenth Durham Light Infantry - William Harrington was reported as killed in action, aged only twenty-two.

This time she knew his parents, John and Isabella, but felt there was nothing she could say or do to ease their pain. She could only imagine how awful it must be to receive the dreaded letter and hoped, prayed even, that it would never happen to her.

At times, loneliness overwhelmed her. She had the children but they didn't provide the company and support she required. She needed a man to love her and satisfy her longings. But would her husband ever return? She had almost convinced herself that he wouldn't. Surely there was more to life than her present empty existence. Looking after four children, alone, was as far removed from her ideal as she could possibly have imagined. She loved her children but she also yearned for her freedom. Hadn't she known too much sadness in her past to allow herself to be so miserable now? And wasn't there still so much more to life to discover than be so tied down with children in the future?

She began to have a change of heart. Instead of hiding herself away, she decided that some adult company was what she required. Maybe this would help her forget her troubles and bring her some much-needed relief from the on-going drudgery of her life. It seemed such a long time since she had experienced any physical contact with John-George and she wondered just how long it would be before she would again - if at all. The thought of being unfaithful was not something that she would ever contemplate, would she?

She chided herself for even considering such a notion but felt sure she wasn't alone in having these desires and yearnings to be with a man. For she still liked to think she was pleasant looking even if she'd lost her fresh youthful complexion and was hopeful that her figure belied the fact she had given birth to four children. She could, she assured herself, be mistaken for a woman much younger than her twenty-eight years. At her young age, didn't she deserve to be noticed and shouldn't she be enjoying some attention, rather than languishing at home in dull and dreary day to day living?

Then the thought came into her mind - how about taking in a lodger? Not only would it offer her some much needed company, it would also supply her with a small but very necessary additional income. But would there be any takers? Most single women had gone into the towns and cities, to help with the war effort. There were a few men left in the village, those whose employment exempted them from volunteering, those too old or disabled in some way to join up and the 'conchies' of course. Offering one of them a room, she realised, would be classed as most inappropriate. The only other real drawback to this plan, was the lack of space in her home. In order to provide a single room to let, she would need to move into the same bedroom as the children. It would be rather impractical and very cramped but not totally inconceivable.

TWELVE
Bowburn - 1917

Maggie made enquiries and eventually found a man seeking a room to rent who was happy to pay what she asked. She quickly became aware that certain folk were talking about her, suggesting she wasn't just doing it for the money, but she took no notice. Weren't present times hard enough without worrying what others thought about you? Every day it seemed that life was becoming more difficult, not just for her but for everyone in the village.

In February 1917, the Germans were determined to crush the British people by trying to starve them into submission. At first, Maggie was totally oblivious that German U boats were sinking merchant ships, bringing supplies to Britain, causing thousands of tons of food to be lost. But she soon became aware of huge queues at the shops as shortages of the basics such as meat, sugar, butter and flour took hold and prices began to increase.

'I'm sure some folks are hoarding supplies,' Maggie complained to her family but she daren't report them, for fear of reprisal. 'We'll just have to eat more vegetables, instead,' she suggested to the children, but knew it wouldn't go down too well. They loved the cakes their mother made especially her Madeira with its caraway seeds on top.

Maggie was particularly grateful that she was still receiving a free bag of coal each week, in fulfilment of the colliery's promise back in 1914. For there was also a fuel shortage and coal was in such short supply that it was rationed according to the number of rooms in each home.

A complete state of 'war weariness' seemed to be enveloping the whole country, with no obvious end in sight. For Maggie there were constant concerns over the children's welfare, particularly Roland's perpetual struggle with his weak chest and the restrictive cost of medicine. She also fretted about the cost of clothing them and the difficulty she'd had in keeping them warm over the winter. But for Maggie, these anxieties were nothing compared to what was about to face her.

It was early on a Thursday morning, May 17th 1917, that she heard a loud knocking at the door. Slightly annoyed at the disruption, she reluctantly went over to answer it. It was the postman waiting to hand over a buff coloured envelope. Initially

Maggie was delighted, thinking it may be the longed for letter from her husband but the large bold print **'On His Majesty's Service'** told her differently. She froze for a moment and took a sharp intake of breath. She was fully aware of exactly what news might be contained within. She'd learnt from other mothers and wives that the postman was assigned to bring bad news to the families of those soldiers who were in the lower ranks. The telegram boy, on his bike, painted blood red for urgency, was only sent to families whose sons and husbands were officers. She hastily pushed the envelope down the front of her blouse. She needed a few minutes to quieten herself. By leaving it unopened, she felt she could maintain a flicker of hope that it may not be regarding John-George. It was only later that morning, when the children were outside playing, that she carefully removed it, her hands shaking in trepidation.

Slowly her eyes scanned the contents, trying to allow the words to sink in:

'It is my painful duty to inform you that a report has been received from the War Office notifying the death of John-George Purvis on Thursday, May 10th 1917.'

The words became a blur as the tears flowed. She read on, something about her husband being *'missing in action,'* and offering *'their deepest sympathy.'*

Maggie was totally, utterly distraught. She fell to her knees, screaming and sobbing hysterically. Was it true? This cold, impersonal piece of paper, telling her such dreadful news. She didn't want to believe it and yet...

For the rest of that day, numbed by grief, Maggie just sat and stared at the slip of paper, unable to eat, unable to think and barely able to move. Was she really never to see John-George again? Would she never hear the sound of his voice or feel the tenderness of his touch? She read the words over and over again. There was nothing to tell her how or where he'd died but just a slow realisation, that the news she'd been dreading for so long, had now arrived. He was not going to be one of those fortunate ones to be spared.

He was DEAD.

Maggie forced herself out of the armchair where John-George had last sat and went over to the mantelpiece. She took the photo, the one he'd had taken in his army uniform, and with tears streaming down her face, she turned it around .She could no longer bear to look at it.

Realising the children, particularly Jacob, might be aware that all was far from well, she decided it was time they knew the truth. She gathered the children together that evening, determined to relate some of the awful news but wondering just how much to divulge to them.

'I have something to tell you,' she began hesitantly but realising the children had no notion of what was to come, she just blurted it out,

'Your da won't be coming back,' she said, as her body was wracked with sobs.

'Not coming back?' Roland repeated.

'Why not?' asked Ann, unsure quite what she meant.

'Cos' he's dead, isn't he?' Jacob snapped back angrily and with that he stormed out of the house.

Roland, seeing his mother so upset, rushed over to give her a loving embrace. He was too young to truly understand but he had always shown that maturity beyond his years and now sensed his mother's pain. She was too overcome to respond appreciatively but simply stroked him on the head as she sat lost in her own morbid thoughts. The children soon resumed their playful activities, unaware that this was a redefining moment in their lives, for in truth their father had been absent for most of their existence and they knew no different.

As for Jacob, he returned some hours later but spoke nothing of his initial reaction and his heartbroken feelings. Maggie felt it best to ignore him, to allow him come to terms with his father's loss in his own way. But she noticed, soon afterwards, the photograph was back in its rightful position.

Over the following days, Maggie lived on autopilot, but as the initial shock and numbness began to lessen, it was replaced by a search for answers and a clinging to hope. She wondered and even began to pray that just maybe the War Office had got it wrong and that her husband wasn't dead.

Different scenarios raced through her head. Did '*missing in action*' necessarily mean he was deceased? Maybe there was a possibility that John-George had been knocked out and lost his memory. Maybe he was lying in some foreign hospital bed, injured but still alive. Maybe he had been captured and taken prisoner but was unharmed. Maybe even, they'd identified a deceased man incorrectly and that it wasn't John-George's body they were referring to?

Maggie's mind buzzed with so many diverse possibilities - all of them more palatable than the one she had been given. She found herself awaiting the post every day just hoping there might be a letter, either from her husband or from an officer informing her there'd been a mistake. But she waited in vain.

As days passed by, along with her grief, came an overwhelming feeling of guilt and self-loathing. She tortured herself with regret. Why had she even considered being with another man when the only real love she had ever known was for John-George? Yes, she had been so young when they met and she'd been duty bound to marry him when he'd got her 'with child', but she had genuinely loved him. She must, she told herself, acknowledge this fact by putting a tribute in the local paper.

So on 1st June, when she had almost accepted the truth that he was not returning, she placed an announcement in 'The Durham Advertiser' declaring her deep love:

<u>*John-George Purvis*</u>

Killed in action May 10th 1917, aged 33.
Dearly loved husband of Margaret Purvis,
1 Wylam Street, Bowburn.
Death divides but memory clings. Rest in peace.

Rest in Peace! Maggie found that phrase so difficult to accept and bad thoughts tormented her. How could he be, at rest, when he had no grave? Where was he lying? The body of John-George had not been found so what had happened to him? Margaret persecuted herself with dreadful images. She lay in bed at night, her mind re-enacting the scene of his final minutes. She tortured herself with horrific pictures of suffering and a slow, agonising death from horrendous wounds. She wondered if he'd thought of her and the children, as his life had ebbed away, or worse still, if he'd cried out her name in his final moments.

In the following days, Maggie came to dread waking up in the morning, as the enormity of her loss dawned on her. All she wanted was to withdraw from those around her and stay cocooned in the release that sleep brought.

* * * * *

'Mother, there's a letter arrived for you,' she heard Jacob call up to her one morning as she struggled, yet again, to get out of bed.

'A letter?' Maggie cried out as she jumped up hastily and dashed down the stairs. Letters were such a rarity and she felt a rush of both excitement and foreboding as two contrasting possibilities raced through her mind. Either it was from John-George meaning he was alive after all or it was confirmation that that his body had been found and that meant...

Maggie snatched the envelope rather impolitely from Jacob's hand and studied the handwriting. She didn't recognise it; that wasn't a good start. She fumbled as she tore it open exposing a single sheet of paper. She stumbled over the words as her mind raced ahead.

Dear Mrs Purvis,

This is to inform you that…

Inform her of what? She perused the words with difficulty, so many of them challenging for her to read but she told herself to slow down, despite her eagerness to ascertain its contents.

It said something about an eviction and her need to gather together all her personal belongings. What! Was her understanding of the contents correct? Was she really to be thrown out of her home and by the look of the date, it was due to happen the following week.

'No! No! This can't be true,' she yelled, gesticulating wildly.

'Whatever's the matter?' Jacob asked, as he witnessed her violent reaction.

'Not only have we lost your da, it seems we're to lose the house as well,' she yelled.

'Why?' he asked, alarmed at the thought and then continued, 'Where will we go?' not appreciating that the timing of such a question was inappropriate.

'I don't bloody know!' his mother retorted, 'but I do know it's not bloody fair.'

'Well, let's just stay put then,' Jacob replied naively.

Maggie became lost in her thoughts. Hadn't the mining company promised she could stay in the house whilst John-George was fighting abroad. Just because he'd been killed was surely not justification for forcing her to leave – in fact, it was more important than ever, that she had a roof over her head. Besides she knew of other families that had stayed put despite losing their breadwinner. Why had she been targeted? Perhaps if she offered to pay more rent they might allow her to stay, she could perhaps spare a few coppers from the money she made with the lodger.

Then it dawned on her! The lodger! Could he be the reason she had received such a letter? Feelings of guilt surfaced and the realisation that it might be solely her fault that her children were about to become homeless. She must do something, anything…

Her first thought was to race over to her in-laws' house to share this latest agony with them. She knew there was no possibility of ever moving in with them- space was so limited - but at least she could talk over her problem … or so she hoped.

After giving Jacob clear instructions to stay and look after the youngsters, she rushed off down the street. When John, her father-in-law, opened the door, after hearing her frantic hammering, he didn't give her quite the welcome she'd expected.

'Ann's most unwell, can you come back another day?' he requested, not even inviting her over the doorstep.

'What's wrong with her?' Maggie enquired when she saw how anxious John seemed.

'It's hit your mother-in-law really hard to lose her two sons. Do you know her hair virtually turned white overnight and she's hardly eaten anything these past few weeks? I don't think she'll ever get over losing the boys, in fact she's saying she doesn't want to go on...'

Maggie didn't know how to react. She knew there was no point in sharing her own troubles but felt unable to comfort John. Didn't she have enough worries of her own? In fact right at that moment, she was experiencing similar thoughts herself...

THIRTEEN
The outskirts of Bowburn - Summer 1917

The morning, when she awoke in the army bell tent, after being evicted, Maggie knew greater despair than she had ever experienced; for her there was no future. Her former life with its share of ups and downs, paled into insignificance compared to what she imagined might lie ahead. No breadwinner and four children who were totally dependent on her was an intolerable, desperate situation.

She couldn't accept that other war widows, living in rented accommodation, hadn't been told to leave their home. Once again, she was asking herself why they had singled her out for such treatment.

The same re-occurring thought came to her - perhaps, just perhaps, somebody in her street, had betrayed her to the mining authorities. Had that nosy neighbour who'd been watching her, reported her, relaying the fact that she'd had a man living in her house. That, she concluded, could be a reason why they'd ordered her to leave her home, believing that she was not the destitute and upstanding widow she was professing to be. She had no proof of course but similarly she had no way of disproving it. She was more than angry about her eviction but knew she had no strength left in her to argue against it.

There was however a minor encouragement, just one shred of comfort, in that she wasn't the only one suffering the indignity of eviction. There were a couple of other women with young children, using the tents as temporary accommodation, because they'd too found themselves without a home. Maggie didn't like to enquire the reason behind their predicament but one of them, introduced herself as Mrs Snook, a widow with three young children. Maggie didn't recognise her but she found her to be a kindly woman with a broad grin and a friendly demeanour.

'You're new 'ere aren't you? Well I'm Mrs Snook but call me Edith,' she said pleasantly, adding, 'I can imagine how you're feeling right now, as I guess, like me, you've just lost your husband.'

Maggie nodded. She wasn't used to sympathy and she had to work hard to hold back the tears.

Mrs Snook was soon sharing her individual story of hardship

and was eager to give advice. Being in a similar situation, with a growing family to support, she was adamant that they must be entitled to some financial help:

'Us widows should surely qualify for an army pension - we must make enquiries and soon. We definitely deserve it after what they've put our poor boys through!'

There was also another single mother, with two children, but she was more aloof and barely passed two words with Maggie. However, her wayward son was more forthcoming and quickly became Jacob's newly found ally. The lad, barely thirteen but appearing older, had an arrogant air and was full of bravado. Maggie had real misgivings about the friendship, especially when she overheard him boasting that he might go off to enlist in the army and stupidly suggested that Jacob might like to join him! Maggie wanted to warn Jacob off but with his mother not far away, she felt it best to hold her counsel. Best not cause enemies she thought - well not yet at least.

Mrs. Snook, in contrast, told her young son, in no uncertain terms, that he was not to wander off with the lads. To ensure her orders were obeyed, she set him on cleaning the boots for her entire family of five. He readily complied but whilst Jacob showed no willingness to follow his example, Roland soon volunteered to try and do something with his own sodden footwear and that of his mother's. However, Jacob was not going anywhere, not for the moment at least.

'I need you to stay around Jacob,' ordered Maggie after a morning spent in hectic and somewhat heated conversation, 'You gotta look after the bairns whilst I go down to army depot. I'm going to see if I can claim some money for your father's bravery.'

Jacob scowled rudely but knew he'd do best to obey, if he wanted his freedom later.

He was also more willing to comply because it was to do with his 'da'. Although he'd been just six when his father had left home, he remembered him with love and respect. Admittedly he hadn't seen that much of him, due to his long hours spent at work, but he recalled every night on his father's return, it had been his job to fetch the tin bath from outside and fill it with water. Then his father had bathed in front of the fire, asking his son to help wash away the day's dust and grime, with one exception,

'Remember to leave a strip of muck down the full length of me back,' his da repeated, every single evening.

Jacob had soon realised it was a superstition of all the miners, believing that it strengthened their backs.

Jacob had enjoyed this time with his da and he'd also

appreciated that his da never insisted that he, or his brother and sister went to school. Being semi -literate himself, he didn't particularly value education so Jacob had been allowed to spend time at home, as long as he completed his chores. In Jacob's mind, cleaning boots, seeing to the fire and sweeping the yard had been far more preferable than being confined within a classroom.

However, he hadn't enjoyed the workload of all the past months and years, since his father had gone off to fight. He hated being the oldest child, simply because it meant more was expected of him. If his mother had her way, he would he felt, be working non-stop.

If only his da was here now, things would be so different, Jacob thought, but deep down he realised that he would never see him again. The hurt he felt went deep but he vowed never to show it. Jacob did love his family, especially his younger sister, but he hated this present situation and what he perceived as his enforced new role as replacement da. He was really starting to take exception to his mother's constant demands. But these negative feelings were nothing compared to what was to come. Over the next few months this resentment of his mother would turn to hatred - a hatred more deep and all consuming than he could ever have imagined.

FOURTEEN
Bowburn - Autumn 1917

Maggie felt determined to discover if Mrs. Snook was indeed correct in her belief that an army pension was available . In fact by the time she arrived at the army depot, she was fuelled up and ready to fight her corner. She was adamant that John-George's bravery should be acknowledged - after all her husband had given his life for 'King and Country'.

She queued in an orderly line, waiting along with other widows to find out what would ultimately decide her future. Even if she was entitled to a pension, how much would it be - enough to provide for her growing family?

When her turn eventually came, a feeling of frustration swamped her. She had four demanding children and now she was dependent on a positive result.

The young officer spoke to her kindly and after ascertaining her name, he gently enquired,

'What were the circumstances of your husband's death?'

Maggie, nervous and defensive, told his story as much as she knew.

'Blown to bits, I reckon,' she paused. 'Blown to bits, just in an instant and missing forever,' she repeated, as if the telling of it twice would help her cause.

The officer listened patiently but showed little emotion. To him, it was just another similar tale of woe, which he'd heard repeated numerous times before. For this was not just about one individual's suffering as there were many families, within Bowburn alone, where there was no longer a husband or father. Nearly every story he'd listened to that morning was regarding some personal catastrophe and it was mind numbing.

Maggie, when she finally completed her plea, felt quite overcome. Just the telling of it aroused painful feelings but it was so important she got her message across. She must have succeeded because she suddenly realised what the officer was saying:

'You are indeed entitled to compensation for the loss of your husband. As you have four dependent children, I am happy to award you a weekly pension of twenty-three shillings and six pence.'

He produced a grey form, printed in black and comprising

several pages. Maggie's heart sank at the thought of having to complete it with her limited skills.

'I'll complete the claim form for you, as long as you give me all the relevant details,' she heard the man say helpfully, 'all you'll have to do is sign it - or put your mark,' he added, realising she was struggling. Maggie nodded appreciatively,

'Thank you,' she whispered, although she really didn't want to relate all her husband's personal details, it was too harrowing.

At first Maggie was grateful and optimistic that this pension might be the answer to her problems. But as she walked away, she pondered on the money – would it be enough to provide for all of her own plus her children's needs? A single tear coursed down her face. It was tortuous for Maggie to know her beloved husband would never again meet his last child or indeed watch any of his children grow up.

Yes he'd volunteered to fight with such hope - and a gallant determination to halt the Germans but he had sacrificed his life in the process. Now all she was left with, were four young children to bring up on her own, with no breadwinner and no home. Was that really all his life was worth? Twenty-three shillings and sixpence and a brusque note sent with the postman. Maggie was still smarting from that brief, terse letter and today she felt the pain of it more than ever. It was certainly no substitute for the loss of her dearest John-George.

Maggie took her time before going back to the tent. She called at the shop and purchased a few necessities. She wanted to buy medicine for Roland but it was so very expensive. She had to keep some money back for emergencies. It was well past mid-day when she returned to the children. She hoped that they'd be so excited at her news of the financial award that they'd not notice her tear stained face.

'Where's that brother of yours? Maggie demanded when she realised that Jacob was missing.

'With his mates!' Roland replied. Maggie was furious.

'You mean he didn't stay to look after you, as I asked him to do?'

Roland shook his head but felt no guilt at betraying his brother.

'He's been gone ages,' Roland continued, rubbing it in, knowing full well that he was causing even more trouble for his elder sibling.

'Just wait 'til he gets back, he'll not be so happy then,' his mother replied, with a venom that surprised him.

That evening, after the younger children had gone to bed,

Maggie decided she would accept William and Rob's invitation for a drink. She felt in need of some comfort - even if it was to be sought by means of a bottle. She ordered Jacob not to go out with his new found friend, partly by way of punishment, but also as she expected him to keep his eye on the younger ones. She felt no guilt about this, as at nine years old, she considered he was more than capable of looking after them, especially as she only intended to leave them for a short while.

Her head soon felt light as, all too hurriedly, she downed her first gin - but at least her dark mood began to lift. She shared the day's events with the men and just the telling of them, helped to calm her. William further encouraged her to relax and forget her troubles with more drink and Robert gave her a refill. The few minutes quickly turned to an hour but Maggie wasn't concerned, indeed she was enjoying herself. The night air brought a chill but despite this, Maggie felt warm and jovial. Rob suggested he go to the alehouse for 'a drop more of the good stuff', leaving Maggie and William to chat.

Maggie caught herself staring at William, as they conversed easily, perched on a couple of orange boxes. In the dull lamp light she guessed he was a good ten years older than her twenty-eight years. If not, he certainly looked it! Many years down the mine, she decided, had taken their toll on his complexion and his lean, bent figure plus his persistent cough, suggested his health had suffered too. Despite this, he had obviously been a good-looking man. His dark hair was swept back against a sallow skin and his deep blue eyes were piercing and friendly. In many ways he reminded her of John-George, especially with his charming manner, although he was much taller. William didn't seem to be aware that she was analysing him but continued to chat away, although when she did finally speak, he gave her his full attention. She couldn't help noticing his eyes, as they fixed intently on her, making her feel slightly uncomfortable.

'Maybe it's time I went back to the bairns' she mused, 'it's getting late and knowing Jacob, he will have scarpered. Thanks for a good evening,' she added as she turned to go.

'Just wait Maggie, the evening doesn't have to end yet,' William replied as he grabbed her arm.

Suddenly, quite unexpectedly, she found herself held in a tight grip and being kissed rather forcibly. She pulled away quickly, angry at his roughness and his assumption that this was acceptable and she was willing.

'What's up with you Maggie, do you not realise how attractive you are!' he laughed.

'Maybe so,' she replied 'but I ain't anybody's for the taking,' and with that she stood up, rubbed a scruffy sleeve across her face and made again as if to leave. William caught her arm but this time more gently.

'Why, you can give a man a bit of a kiss, can't you?' he remonstrated.

'What will Rob think, he'll be back any minute,' Maggie suggested, but this was greeted with a derisory laugh.

'What! Rob back in a minute? You don't think he'd come back when there's a warm ale house to stay in. Now come here!' and with that she found herself being forced downwards onto the tent floor…

By the time Maggie returned to her tent, Roland's asthma had worsened but she was too intoxicated to be concerned. She cradled him close and immediately fell asleep. She slumbered deeply with the drink and heard no more of Roland's ruttlings. In the morning she encouraged all the children, especially Roland, to go out into the weak September sunshine. The warmth of it was minimal but the air was fresh and besides she wanted rid of them for a while. She felt distinctively unwell and needed some space.

Over the following weeks, she became increasingly despondent as she tried to decide on her plan of action when all she could see was a black hole. Everyday tasks were a constant struggle and her temper was definitely becoming shorter. Jacob made no allowances and took advantage of her inability to discipline him, at every opportunity. Answering back to every demand, refusing most of the time to comply with each request and generally disregarding all her instructions, he became a law unto himself.

Roland conversely, was compliant but greatly hampered by his constant struggle for breath. John-George, still only a toddler, was also hard work simply because of his very existence and his on-going need for attention and provision. Ann was always willing to help her mother with the everyday tasks but she couldn't give her mother the comfort she needed.

Why had John-George ever volunteered to fight in the war? This question plagued her day and night. He had gone with patriotism and hope but his dedication had merely resulted in death and all she was left with was a pension and nothing else. Yes, she was still dwelling on the harshness of twenty-three shillings and sixpence, it barely went anywhere with four children to support.

Maggie continued to feel full of self-pity and despair when she was given news that rocked her further. Out one morning, she bumped into John, her father-in-law.

'I'm glad I've seen you Maggie, I've been told that you lost your home, but I wasn't sure where you'd gone, none of my neighbours seemed to know, ' he told her.

Before she had time to respond, he explained,'I wanted to see you, I don't expect you've heard have you Maggie?' His voice began to falter as he added, 'Ann died last week. She just sat in her chair one evening and never got up. I reckon she died of a broken heart, she loved her boys so much.'

Maggie was shocked and gasped in horror. She could certainly identify with her mother in law's unbearable pain.

'She never deserved to have so much sorrow,' Maggie said sympathetically, placing her hand on his arm, 'this whole war just seems so futile to me, their deaths just pointless.'

'Yes, what a sacrifice our country has demanded of them,' John remarked. 'And to think our poor Henry and John-George are lying out there somewhere on bare soil, with no coffin, not even a pauper's grave…' but then as tears began to fill his eyes, he made his excuse to walk on. Maggie realised there were no adequate words of comfort that she could give and there was definitely no point in adding to his troubles by relating how awful things were for her, so she let him go.

An all-consuming despair began to surface in Maggie that she found hard to control. Whatever would she have to face next? She didn't want to think of a future if this was all life had to offer her - heartbreak and suffering - was there any point in continuing? Maybe it would be best if she went the same way as Ann but then she reminded herself, there were the children to consider. Would they have a better future without her?

Over the next few days, Maggie's turmoil escalated until she was totally exhausted. Sleep evaded her and her mind continually raced with unwelcome thoughts. But then she reminded herself of a previous time when she'd felt similar anguish and pain. It was way back in her childhood, when her father had deserted her when she was nine, causing her to feel rejected and bereft. She'd reached rock bottom then and yet hadn't she'd survived, whilst still being merely a minor. Surely, she chided herself, there must be a way forward this time as well.

Slowly an idea began to surface - a belief that there must be something better on offer than how she was living now. Just that thought alone gave her some relief. Did she have to go on living under these conditions or was there a means of escape that was within her grasp?

It wouldn't be an easy solution but it was a possible one...

FIFTEEN
Pelton - 1917

'We're going to call on your grandparents, Jacob and Marian,' Maggie announced one Sunday morning, I think a visit to Pelton might do us all good. It's a long way but we haven't seen them for ages, so it's time for a catch up.'

Maggie gathered up a bundle of clothes, hoping they might be invited to stay over for a few nights and ordered the children to find some footwear and to dress in their 'Sunday best', not that they had clothes that could be deemed particularly smart.

'Aw, do we have to go, ma, I'd other plans?' Jacob protested vehemently at first, but then he conceded, thinking that he might get a decent meal at his grandparent's home, something that he hadn't enjoyed for several days.

On the way out of the field, they passed William and Rob's tent, but with her mind elsewhere, Maggie didn't even look in their direction. She had seen little of them since 'that night' and for that she was grateful.

The cart ride to Pelton, a village six miles north of Durham, seemed to take an age and was most uncomfortable. Despite this, Jacob whooped with delight as he felt every bump of the uneven terrain, causing his stomach to lurch repeatedly. Maggie, on the other hand, felt rather queasy and protested to the driver to take it easy. She was in a particularly sombre mood and her thoughts turned, yet again, to how much easier her life would be without her children. She loved them deeply but they certainly deserved a better life than the one they were having now. If she had no dependants it would provide her with the opportunity to find employment and make a fresh start. That prospect was quite appealing.

These transitory thoughts soon evaporated as she and the children were reunited with family. Maggie was quite shocked by how much her father had aged, forgetting that he was now in his sixty fourth year. His once bright ginger hair had turned completely white, although it was mostly hidden under his flat cloth cap. It was more his full snowy moustache that revealed this transition. Despite his slight build, he'd always been very upright and strong. Now he seemed less imposing with his stooped back, his round shoulders and his ambling gait with rather bandy legs, caused no doubt by many years working in such confined spaces in the pit. Although Maggie had harboured a certain resentment towards him after his 'desertion' of her and the other siblings, she still had a genuine fondness for her father. He'd always had a warm side and a great sense of humour that she was pleased to see he hadn't lost:

'Just look at how you kids have grown,' he said as he gave each child in turn a massive hug. 'Now let's have a look at your fizzogs,' he teased, using an expression from his Cumberland days. The children looked up at him, puzzled but amused as he continued.

'And I see three of you are carrot tops - just like I used to be once!' he said, laughing as he ruffled Roland's hair.

'It's brown hair!' Roland insisted.

'What's that? What's not fair?' Jacob asked and Maggie instantly remembered her father's loss of hearing.

'Grandfather won't always hear what you say,' she explained to the children quietly, so as not to offend him.

Although the children barely knew their granddad, they quickly felt at ease with him and were soon fighting for his affection. He instantly had a soft spot for Ann who had her own sense of fun and he whisked her up in the air, making her giggle with delight.

'Me! Me!' shrieked John-George, holding his arms aloft, and even the more serious Roland clung to his grandfather's trouser leg. Jacob was indifferent and quickly discovered his grandfather's briarwood pipe to play with.

Maggie was more reticent with Marian but even she seemed to have mellowed with the passing of time. She was a small, stout woman with a neat appearance. Her greying hair was pulled back into a tidy bun and her simple clothes were covered by a large flowery apron. It appeared to Maggie, she was genuinely pleased to see them and all the family enjoyed a satisfying meal that night and for that reason alone, Maggie knew the visit was worthwhile. But she had more on her mind than food. She wanted to ask a favour from her stepmother and father, a very special favour but approaching it wasn't going to be easy.

Aware that she'd not been in contact for many months, Maggie was unsure how sympathetic they would be to her present plight. But then if she didn't verbalise her wishes, she'd never know their response and it may just be positive. After all Maggie had never wanted or intended to find herself in a situation where she couldn't provide for her family and it wasn't of her own doing. There was, she told herself, no point in holding back, the truth had to be faced. She simply couldn't cope with four children, with limited funds and no husband to provide for them.

After a couple of days, with her visit drawing to a close, Maggie finally found the courage to reveal the true reason for her visit:

'I was wondering if I could ask a big favour of you? Can I leave Ann with you for a while?' she asked Marian tentatively, after revealing some of her present predicament.

'It'll only be a temporary measure, 'til I get me self sorted out,' she promised.

Jacob looked at Marian with one of his familiar blank stares and she instantly knew that he hadn't heard any of what had been said. She repeated Maggie's request and they waited for his response. It seemed to be an age before he nodded,

'Aye all right lass,' he muttered but said nothing else. Out of all the children, he was happiest to take on Ann for she was an easy going and contented child and he felt she'd be no trouble for a few weeks. Aware that he was almost an old age pensioner, he had some silent reservations but then the childcare would never be down to him and he knew that.

Ann herself was quite shocked at this turn of events. Had her mother planned this before they set off? Was that why she'd insisted Ann bring some extra clothes along with her? She liked her grandfather and she accepted Marian as her grandmother yet she hadn't bargained on staying with them. She didn't like the thought of being parted from her brothers particularly from John-George whom she liked to fuss over.

'When will I see you again?' she asked her mother when she was given a brief goodbye hug.

'You be a good girl and do as you're told,' her mother replied, ignoring her question, as in truth she wasn't sure of the honest answer.

'I will ma,' Ann replied compliantly, 'but please promise me that I'll see you all again soon,' she begged, embracing each brother in turn. Her voice quivered with emotion and for a moment, Maggie felt gripped by guilt at her actions but then she reminded herself this was a much better option for Ann than their present situation.

As they travelled home, Maggie felt a certain sadness but her over riding feeling was one of relief – this first part of her plan had been successful at least. But this had been relatively easy. Deciding on the future of the three boys was much more of a problem, especially Jacob with his challenging behaviour. She accepted this might be partly her fault. Having lost her own mother when she was so young, she'd never had a role model to demonstrate how a good mother should discipline her children. Perhaps she was lax in what she let the boys get away with. At least, the two younger ones were still malleable and generally easier to control, so maybe, Maggie concluded, Roland and John-George were still adaptable enough to accept going into an orphanage. Although she hated the thought of it, she was reassured, knowing they would have regular meals and a warm bed every night. She was sure that Roland would do a good job of looking after his younger brother. It could even lead to an improvement in his health as hopefully he would get the necessary medical attention and... Maggie continued to find justifiable reasons for adopting this idea. She knew of a suitable home too - it was in Durham and run by the Poor Law Institution. It was well known in the city for its adoption of 'waifs and strays'. Maggie felt it wasn't a permanent solution, just a 'temporary measure', at least that's what she told herself, more to assuage her guilt than thinking it was a definite truth.

Maggie didn't mention this idea to the boys but fully intended to carry it out within the week. She decided to take them into the village first, planning to buy them some new underwear, as she was particularly ashamed of what they were wearing at present, Jacob's hand me downs and more than well worn.

Whilst out on her errands, she bumped into her sister-in-law, Jenny, who still lived nearby in Clarence Street. Her husband Arthur was a miner and they had two children, although both grown up and long since left home. Jenny had instantly taken to Maggie when John-George first introduced the two of them, at his parent's home, some ten years earlier. They had been friendly ever since and Maggie trusted Jenny and felt able to confide in her. She told her how difficult life had become since John-George's death, followed by the unexpected eviction:

'I don't know what you'll think of me but I'm considering leaving Roland and John-George at the orphanage for a while. I need to work and then I can afford lodgings. There's no way I can do that with the children needing me all the time,' she explained.

Jenny listened sympathetically. She nodded her head in agreement. But her reply was still unexpected:

'Would it help if I looked after them, if you think it's just temporary. I'm sure Arthur won't mind, besides it'll be me who'll take most care of them,' she volunteered with a wry smile.

Maggie didn't hesitate. This was an offer she accepted readily for she knew the two younger boys would settle happily with their Aunt Jenny and Uncle Arthur:

'You're a good one Jenny Brooks I can't thank you enough,'

she said with genuine sincerity but then adding a promise which she had little intention of fulfilling:

'I'll be back to collect them as soon as things improve.'

The two of them hugged and chatted freely, making arrangements for the end of the week when she'd hand the boys over. Maggie's spirits lifted as they said their goodbyes. It seemed her arrangements for the boys were working out better than she'd anticipated. She smiled to herself - best still go buy that new underwear though, it wouldn't do for Jenny to think badly of her!

That evening she sat the two younger boys down and explained as best she could what was going to happen,

'I thought you two might like a holiday,' was how she put it to them.

The boys were immediately interested, excited even, as they'd never had one, but what they didn't realise, was that they were going by themselves.

'I'm sending you to your Aunt Jenny and Uncle Arthur's house for a few weeks. They're going to look after you whilst your mother finds some work. Then we'll be able to rent a place and be back together.'

'What about Jacob?' Roland enquired.

'Don't you worry about him,' was all Maggie would say.

They seemed to accept it, Roland more so than John-George, who was still too young to fully comprehend what his mother was telling him.

The following day, Maggie encouraged the boys to gather together their few personal belongings, items of clothing mainly plus Roland picked up his toy cart and John-George found his spinning top. She brushed their hair and made sure their faces were scrubbed and their shoes clean. Then she marched them down the road to Clarence Street.

Aunt Jenny was pleased to see them and she greeted them warmly,

'Come in! Come in!' she enthused, 'why you two do look smart.'

Maggie decided to make the goodbyes as brief as possible,

'Will we see you again soon ma?' Roland asked, as his mother patted him on the head and told them she was going.

'I'm sure you will,' Maggie said hugging him gently.

Roland put a comforting arm around his brother, as he began to wail,

'Ma's only a few streets away, we're bound to see her again soon,' he told him trying to be positive.

But deep down Roland had his own doubts. Wise for his

years, he sensed his mother was eager to be free of them. In recent months he'd witnessed things he shouldn't have and watched as his mother's care for her children - and her mood - had deteriorated.

In many ways Roland was correct in his assumptions. Maggie was indeed ready to free herself of the children so that she could start again. She still had the tricky problem of what to do with Jacob and acknowledged that this part of her scheme was going to be the most difficult. She recognised that bringing up Jacob had been an endless struggle, particularly since his da had left home. He needed a firm hand that was for sure. He was often indolent and preferred to be out with his friends than help her in any way. He had a fiercely independent streak, although barely ten and he was far too defiant to go willingly into an institution. What was she to do with him? Who would want him? There were no other relatives to call on - her sisters and brothers had large families of their own, so the financial aspect alone would surely deter them.

So for Maggie, there was only one option. The following day, she persuaded Jacob to go into Durham with her, under a false pretext. On their arrival in the town centre, she thrust a sixpence into Jacob's hand.

'Just go buy yourself a bun, at that baker's over there... and you can keep the change,' she added as an afterthought. Jacob was taken aback. Being spoilt wasn't a feeling he was familiar with but he was happy to do exactly as his mother requested. As he turned his back on her and sped off into the distance, Maggie hesitated for a brief moment. She had real pangs of guilt at the thought of what she was about to do. Despite the antagonism between them, she loved her first born son. Wasn't he the product of that wonderful first union with John-George and she imagined what her husband would have thought, if he had been aware of her cruel intentions. But this was not a time to be soft, for she genuinely felt she had no other choice. She had to maintain a cold detachment in order to survive.

Once Jacob was out of sight, she turned around and walked off in the opposite direction, telling herself not to look back. She mustn't relent for this was her only option. Hadn't her own father abandoned her at a similar age and she'd pulled through. Knowing that Jacob was equally resilient, she was sure he'd find the strength within himself to cope.

When Jacob returned to the busy street and realised his mother had gone, he suddenly felt very vulnerable. His eyes scanned the sea of unfamiliar faces with no sight of her anywhere. Was she in another shop? He waited for what seemed an age but with every passing minute he became more convinced that she had deserted him. He was tempted to cry out to the passers-by, 'I've lost my mother.' But what was the point? They were too preoccupied to even notice him; besides who would care about a young boy they didn't recognise? If his own mother didn't appear to want him, why would anyone else?

The thought of finding his own way back to Bowburn drifted into his mind but was soon dismissed as being equally futile. For in truth, he knew there was no one in the village who'd feel for him enough to offer him a home. He certainly didn't want to go grovelling to his mother, to beg her to rethink. He tried hard to fight back tears but they still filled his eyes and for a while he stood, transfixed to the spot. Yet it wasn't long before his self-pity was replaced by a deep and growing resentment.

How could his mother, a mother who supposedly loved him, do such a callous act? An anger boiled inside him and an all-consuming hatred filled his heart. He vowed there and then, never to forgive her... but for now he had to concentrate on his own survival.

SIXTEEN
Bowburn – Spring 1918

On her return to Bowburn, Maggie felt an aching void but also a great sense of relief. No longer need she worry about finances because now she was free to seek employment. Plus as soon as she was earning, it meant she could look into renting a room. But her troubles were certainly not over and she was perturbed by her continuing decline in health. She was struggling anyway with her low mood but in recent weeks, she'd lost her appetite and felt generally unwell. A visit to the doctor was out of the question. Doctors had to be paid for.

She was soon able to secure work, once again, as a nursing attendant, which enabled her to pay for lodgings, a single, furnished room, in a terraced house back in Wylam Street. It was merely coincidence that she was living seven doors away from her former marital home and somewhat a risk to take knowing there were likely to be some wagging tongues and some pointing fingers. She liked to think that friends and family would believe her story that she fully intended to have her children back, once she felt more positive and her circumstances improved. Her mood did slowly begin to lift but not her general well being. She had an idea why she was feeling so unwell but decided to ignore it. Hadn't she said goodbye to her children - maybe forever - and surely such a trauma, she reassured herself, could be responsible for upsetting her whole system.

Over the next month, she worked hard, gained some financial stability and even enjoyed male company again. But the sickness remained and finally after a solid week of vomiting, Maggie had to accept what she had feared. She was expecting a fifth child.

How could this be happening to her? Why, she asked herself, was life so very, very unfair to her? What were her family going to think? She had abandoned four children and now she was expecting another. She guessed who might be responsible but the man himself had no idea and she certainly wasn't going to tell him. In fact she didn't want anyone to find out about 'her condition'. She couldn't bear the shame of hearing people's comments about her having a child so soon after her husband's death. If only people knew the circumstances in which the child had been conceived, maybe then, they wouldn't be so quick to condemn her. But would anyone believe her story? Wasn't it always the woman who was to blame? People seemed to turn a blind eye to a man's indiscretions so there was no point in revealing the truth. No, she vowed, this baby and the name of the father must be entirely her secret, not only now but for always.

For a fleeting moment she considered whether she should try to abort the baby but it wasn't a realistic option, nor a legal one either. Maggie had heard talk of it: women swallowing large amounts of wash powder in gin, others engaging in violent exercise or having scalding baths to induce miscarriage but she knew there were dangers involved. I could even die, she told herself, so the idea was soon forgotten. Besides, despite not wanting to keep the child, she had no desire to cause it any harm. So she convinced herself that the only solution was to get on with life as best she could. Hadn't she always been a survivor? But Maggie knew keeping this baby meant the end of employment and back to where she was before, living in a tent or even worse, the workhouse. There was certainly no welfare benefits available, no means of financial support from the state. So she decided the best option was to conceal the fact that she was in the family way, for as long as possible. She would continue working right up to the delivery and then do what she had to do! She made sure that her clothes were always loosely fitting and she avoided spending any extra time with those she worked alongside. She even starved herself on occasions to prevent any extra weight gain, though she often felt faint and dizzy as a result.

Some months later, on January 25th 1918, Maggie faced the inevitable, having managed to deceive her fellow workers throughout her confinement. A few had commented that she had put on some weight but they thought she'd simply let herself go, knowing she was still grieving for her husband.

Fortunately, it was on a Friday evening, after work, that she became aware of the now familiar signs that the child was on its way. The labour pains racked her body but she knew they had to be endured. Every contraction was bringing the birth nearer but for what? She accepted that once this child was born there was no point in forming any maternal bond. Instead she must distance herself in order to avoid any feelings of affection for the child.

She longed for a midwife to be with her for support but accepted that it wasn't possible to summon anyone. Besides, she couldn't afford the required fee of 7/6d. So instead she made herself some beef tea, knowing it was used in labour to keep up a mother's spirit and then she gave herself a good wash. Suddenly she felt an overwhelming need to lie down, aware that the baby was ready to arrive.

With a final agonising push, she delivered a tiny premature baby. There were no cries - just a deathly silence. Maggie gathered up the child and noted it was a boy. As she did so, the jerk of her arms seemed to bring the baby to life. He coughed and spluttered whilst his blue face slowly turned to a healthier shade of pink. But to Maggie he seemed a weakling. He was under developed with painfully thin limbs and he had papery skin, which was almost transparent. His breathing seemed shallow and for a while Maggie doubted he would survive. She instinctively cradled him close to her warm body but she resisted the urge to let him suckle. Instead she offered the infant a few drops of evaporated milk, which she'd heard it said was as good as breast milk. He was barely able to take it. She had been successful in hiding him as he grew inside her but now his constant hungry cries were in danger of giving her situation away.

Maggie quickly realised the problems she faced were insurmountable. Going to work would be impossible. Even walking to the local shop for provisions meant there was a chance of bumping into a neighbour or work mate. She could leave the child alone whilst she nipped out although it meant taking a risk...

Maggie's solution had to be calculated and cold but she definitely needed to act quickly. At the earliest opportunity, she knew she had to register the child's birth. If she didn't, she knew there'd be a two-pound fine to pay.

The following Wednesday, she found an old army blanket and folded it roughly around the baby. Then nervously and quietly she rushed along the deserted streets, emptier than usual as it was barely daybreak and most folk were still fast asleep in their beds, She walked resolutely, past the houses and shops towards the edge of the village and beyond. She continued walking, for what seemed mile after mile. Her arms ached holding the infant and she longed to put him down. He was whimpering and this added to her sense of frustration. No doubt he was hungry, she decided, but it would be too much of a hindrance to stop and try to give him milk.

As she approached Durham, she rested for a brief moment, trying not to dwell on what she was about to do. Not much further, she consoled herself. She trudged on until she spotted the registration office. As soon as it opened, she went inside.

'Name of the child?' Mr Fleming, the registrar, asked after Maggie explained what she had come for.

'Oswald Purvis,' Maggie answered immediately. She had chosen the name earlier. It wasn't a family name but then she had no intention of keeping him so there was no point in being sentimental.

Then came further questions, including the one she so wanted to avoid,

'Father's name?'

Maggie bit her lip, 'Can you leave it blank?'

She knew it was a criminal offence to name a man on the birth certificate if you weren't married to him. She was tempted to lie and say Oswald was John-George's child but would they believe her? If they discovered he'd been away fighting in France and then lost his life the previous May, they would realise he couldn't possibly be the father.

Maggie was pleased when the certificate was completed and she could leave. She held the child tightly, relieved that he had fallen back to sleep, and set off along the back streets. She gathered pace now but felt a distinct chill as she approached Gilesgate and saw the familiar tall, imposing Victorian building ahead of her. It was the place Maggie feared above all else... the dreaded workhouse. The place you rarely left, once you found your way inside or so she'd been told. She was pleased to see that the street was relatively empty for she felt a deep sense of guilt at what she was about to do. She stood outside the large wooden door and bent over to kiss Oswald's forehead. Feeling the warmth of it, she did it a second time. Then she gently laid him on the doorstep. She placed a simple note on top of him, giving details of his name and age and a simple excuse that she could no longer cope. Then she hurried off without a backward glance. She had to swallow hard to suppress the tears for she was convinced she would never see Oswald again.

Maggie set out on the long journey, back to her small, rented room, feeling desolate but trying hard to stay calm. She felt a weight had been lifted and tried hard to convince herself that she had done the right thing. Now, she reminded herself, she could pursue her life, at least what was left of it. She could return to work as a nursing attendant and earn enough money to keep herself. She persuaded herself that Oswald was better off without her, although she even wondered if he'd survive. Best not think about that too much, she said to herself, realising it would depress her further. And best to lay low for a day or two, as well, in order to avoid contact with anyone who might gossip about her or ask her any awkward questions.

* * * * *

Normality slowly returned to Maggie's life when she was able to resume work. Routine enveloped her day but at night, often

103

unable to sleep, she dwelt on the full impact of her actions. She was aware of how solitary she had become and recognised her need for company. Yet everyone seemed to have their own problems and their mood appeared as low as hers, especially with the constant news of further casualties amongst the Bowburn lads. She was keen to find some happiness, excitement even, amongst all this weariness yet she didn't have either the means or the ideas as to how to raise her spirits.

One thing she was certain about however and that was she had no intentions of finding pleasure with a man, knowing only too well where that could lead. After conceiving Oswald so easily, in such unfortunate circumstances, she vowed never to allow herself to be 'with child' again. Although, the thought, that she must never risk intimacy with another man, was most unpalatable. Almost every day she ached to be held and to be loved. Surely she was too young at twenty-eight to be celibate for the rest of her life.

For now though, she told herself sternly, she must be content. She had no notion that she was about to receive an unexpected visitor who would alter all her plans but not in a way she could ever have imagined.

SEVENTEEN
Bowburn – Autumn 1918

'Hello, are you Maggie Purvis?' the stranger asked, with a friendly smile.

Who was this older man, Maggie wondered, standing at her doorway in his army uniform? She didn't recognise him as being from the local area and yet he knew her by name. Puzzled, Maggie hesitated to answer. Aware of her obvious confusion, the man quickly explained,

'You won't know me but I was a good friend of your late husband John-George. He said I would find you in Bowburn but you took some tracking down. You weren't at the address he gave me!'

Maggie gasped quietly, more through shock than anything else.

'Don't worry, I've not come for any other reason than he asked me to.'

Maggie, realising that talking to a strange man on the doorstep might set tongues wagging, invited him inside, escorting him upstairs, into the single room that was now her home. She ushered him towards the armchair in the corner and bid him to sit down.

'Please take a seat and tell me what this is all about,' she said as she pulled over another chair and positioned it to face him.

'My name's Allan Fenwick,' he began and slowly he relayed a brief family history.

He told her he'd originated from Lincolnshire where he'd been married to Helen and had four children. He'd then moved north, after becoming a widower and joined the Durham Light Infantry. He explained that he'd been stationed side by side with John-George in the trenches and the two had formed a bond of friendship. He related how John-George had asked him a favour. Would he promise to visit his wife and family, if the worst happened and he was killed?

'He wanted you to know,' whispered Allan, 'that he loved you and it tormented him to think how much you might struggle if he were to be killed. So he asked me to make sure you were managing to survive without him and coping with the children.'

Maggie felt rather embarrassed when she had to explain the

circumstances, which had forced her to abandon her children and the hardships she had endured since John-George's death. She omitted the subsequent birth of Oswald - best not give him the wrong impression of her - but instead Maggie emphasised just how much she was missing her husband and how great the loss was proving to be.

Allan listened and showed sympathy. He'd had his difficulties too and explained that he'd had to consider putting his own children into the workhouse, when his wife had died unexpectedly in childbirth, so he didn't condemn her.

'Have you seen them since?' Maggie enquired, as her own thoughts turned to Oswald. Allan declined to answer, simply shaking his head.

Knowing that helped Maggie to feel less guilty. The fact that he'd been forced to leave his children gave them some common ground. But she still had doubts about his authenticity and stared at him in disbelief. Was this truly her husband's friend? He looked much older than John-George and he had the sultry appearance of a traveller, with his straight, jet-black hair and his care worn, wrinkled face, with its sallow skin. He was thick set and stood very upright, with an air of authority. He must be in his late forties, at least, she reckoned and surely too old to be fighting at the front. Yet she was desperate to believe him, for it gave her a personal link to John-George, which was a comforting feeling.

For the next hour, the pair of them talked openly. Maggie was eager to hear everything Allan could tell her about John-George's experiences, even though it was extremely painful at times. She listened as Allan described the monotony of their daily existence. She laughed as he shared the stories of jokes played to keep spirits lifted. She winced as she heard of rats and lice nibbling at toes and infesting clothes. She was horrified by the enormity of the losses and the appalling injuries. He described how men had been shot directly as they'd emerged from the trenches, many experiencing horrific facial injuries causing many to lose their sight or suffering severe burns. He told her about soldiers who were so shell shocked they'd been damaged mentally, unable to escape their traumatic memories.

'Why Maggie they had such a haunted look,' Allan recalled, 'they would just look past you and gaze vacantly into the distance. Some described it as 'a thousand yard stare,' and they would never speak. They could barely stand upright and walked with this like jerky movement. The officers had no choice really but to discharge them.'

'Have you been discharged?' Maggie asked, rather puzzled

that he was wearing his uniform.

'No, I was badly wounded in one of the battles by flying shrapnel. I was lucky enough to be rescued by stretcher-bearers and taken to hospital. Then after a period of recuperation, I was transferred to the Labour Corps.'

He proudly showed her his Silver War badge, which was fastened to the right lapel of his tweed coat.

'It wouldn't do for folks to think I'd not done my bit,' he announced, knowing that the badge served to tell people that he'd fought in the war but had been injured.

Maggie listened intensely, appalled by everything that he'd told her, but there was a more pertinent question eating away at her, which she needed answering, yet Allan hadn't even touched on it.

'Allan, I need to ask you some things and I need you to tell me the truth. What were the exact circumstances of John-George's death? Did he suffer and did he,' she paused and took a deep breath, 'did he die alone or were…'

'I'm sorry Maggie,' Allan interrupted, 'I need to stop you because there's no point in you asking. You see, I wasn't with him on the day he died, it wasn't until that evening that I learnt he was missing.'

Despite hearing this, Maggie was still eager to probe further,

'Was there a chance, no, I mean is there a chance,' she asked tentatively, 'that a body could be wrongly identified?'

Allan hesitated before answering, as he was keen to put it correctly.

'It's unlikely they'd be wrongly identified… but it's possible that some soldiers might have died - be buried even - without their identity being known,' he explained, adding the rider, 'especially for Durham miners.'

'How do you mean?' Maggie asked, intrigued, feeling her heart begin to pound.

Allan tried to explain:

'Your husband told me that when he worked down the mine, he was paid by how many tubs he filled. He wore braces, didn't he, and that's where he kept his 'tallies' so he knew how many tubs he'd got. Now when he was a soldier, he was supposed to wear a dog tag round his neck. That would help identify him if he was wounded or killed. But John-George and his other mining mates wore their dog tags on their braces. Can you imagine the problem this created? If they were killed, the soldier who found him might tell his officer, that he couldn't identify the casualty as he wasn't wearing a dog tag round his neck.'

'So could, could,' Maggie asked, tripping over her words in

hopeful expectation, 'could a soldier be incorrectly announced as dead, simply because a body wasn't properly identified?'

Allan, fully aware of where her questions were leading, didn't want to give her false hope.

'No Maggie, it's unlikely because each officer would know which members of his platoon were missing, even though their individual bodies couldn't be identified. Sadly some men were blown to pieces and their remains just left in the mud but they were still accounted for on the casualty list.'

'That's enough!' a disappointed Maggie insisted, 'please don't tell me any- more, unless you can tell me good news instead.'

'Well it's good news for me, I'm just waiting to be demobbed.'

'And what next?' Maggie enquired, knowing he was a 'foreigner' in these parts.

'I'm hoping to find a job on the land, working around here,' he told her.

'So you don't want to go back to Lincolnshire then?' she enquired, surprised by his response.

'No, not at all. I've actually rented a small room in the next street, Walker Street, in fact, I've suddenly realised, my room actually looks out onto yours!' and with that Allan took hold of her arm and led her to the open window.

'Look,' he continued, 'I can even access your back yard through mine, which will be great for the next time I call!'

Maggie was somewhat surprised by his forthright approach - she wasn't even sure she wanted to see him again but she heard herself saying,

'Yes, I'd like you to call again Allan, it's been good to meet you.'

After his departure, Maggie wept for a long time. Old memories had surfaced and her grief was reopened like an infected wound. She wanted desperately to be held and comforted but there was no one to provide it. Never had being alone, felt so miserable. That night she pined for everything she had lost. She reassured herself that her children were better off without her but she suddenly felt very ashamed over what she had done, especially to Jacob. She'd tried to ignore the unkind words she'd overheard recently in the street but now the words echoed in her head:

'There's that loose woman who's abandoned all her children! How could she?'

She wasn't the bad woman they'd made her out to be, at least that's what she had told herself at the time, but maybe they were right after all - maybe she was heartless and cruel.

Maggie's tears continued. If ever she needed someone to love and take care of her, it was now. It felt as if she was the one who had been abandoned and right now her life seemed so, so pointless.

* * * * *

It was not long after his visit that Maggie saw Allan again, bumping into him along Wylam Street.

'I've been promised some labouring work on the land, just a couple of miles away,' he informed her, 'so you'll perhaps see a bit more of me in the future.'

Maggie smiled at him but wasn't quite sure how to react about seeing him; she had such mixed emotions. He wasn't a man who appealed to her physically, in truth, he didn't excite her in any way but then she was so grateful to him for seeking her out and relaying news of John-George. She also reminded herself of her feelings of isolation, since abandoning Oswald and being shunned by some of the neighbours.

Over the last few weeks she had rarely stepped outside, except when her need for provisions forced her out into the village and then she had barely spoken to anyone. Now that she was back in Bowburn village, she was scared that she might inadvertently bump into Jenny and the boys although she'd heard that they'd moved on. It wasn't that she didn't want to see them, but she was frightened as to how they might react and the pain it might cause her and them. But her enforced solitude meant she was increasingly lonely and dispirited. Perhaps, she concluded, it would be good to see Allan, for surely any company would be better than no company at all.

Throughout late summer, she began to see him on a regular basis. He would call round after work or they'd meet up at the weekend. They would simply chat over a drink and he'd update her on current events. There was no romance but that was not on Maggie's agenda. He shared more of his background and his guilt at being forced to leave his four children. Maggie finally trusted him enough to tell him about Oswald. She appreciated the fact that, after listening to her story, he didn't condemn her and even agreed that it wasn't her fault.

'I think the war led a lot of folk to do things that were out of character,' he told her sympathetically. 'Sexual desire led many men to take advantage of a woman, to satisfy their needs.'

'Are you saying soldiers were unfaithful?' Maggie asked, quite surprised by this revelation, 'how did they have the opportunity?'

'Oh they had the opportunity alright!' Allan explained, 'I

used to watch many of the soldiers go off to pay French women for ten minutes of passion.'

Maggie was shocked and didn't want to think that John-George could possibly have been one of them.

'Not your husband though,' Allan quickly added, on seeing her worried expression.

'He was so pleased that he had met his new son and that you'd decided to give the child his name. I'm sure his thoughts were always of you.'

Maggie felt immediate shame at her own infidelity but she consoled herself with the knowledge that others had chosen willingly to go with a man, whereas she hadn't.

She appreciated Allan's honesty and his understanding and she realised that she was beginning to warm to him and even, in part, to look forward to his visits.

EIGHTEEN
Bowburn – November 1918

Early in November, Allan called on Maggie, bursting with exciting news he couldn't wait to share,

'The war's coming to an end at last Maggie, after four long years. Germany has surrendered and the Kaiser has abdicated and fled to Holland. A cease-fire agreement has been signed in a railway carriage in Compiegne. People are celebrating all over the country. Do you fancy coming for a walk into the village to see what's happening here?'

Maggie fell silent, wondering if he understood the full impact of his words; the news aroused no delight in her. Why would she want to celebrate when she had lost the man she truly loved? She knew her world had altered for ever on the day he was killed and that fact alone had left her joyless.

'No thank you,' she replied trying not to sound as miserable as she felt, 'I'm glad the war is finally over but let's leave it at that.'

Allan accepted her wishes and cut short his visit, realising Maggie was not in the mood for conversation even, let alone partying.

Over the following days, she was relieved to discover that she was not alone in her attitude. It struck her that there was a pervading atmosphere of gloom in the village. Nearly every family, from the richest to the poorest, had suffered the loss of a loved one and were mourning rather than celebrating.

'We've lost forty six Bowburn lads, in total,' Maggie was informed by one of the mothers, as a group of them gathered to discuss recent events. They all shook their heads in despair and many commented on what a tragic waste of so many young lives.

'No doubt that'll mean a shortage of men to work down the pit,' remarked another, seeing beyond their own pain to realise not only the enormity of the losses but the profound effect they would have.

Maggie was upset to hear so many of the men in the village were gone but as for the labour shortage, she initially had no sympathy for the colliery. She had only bad thoughts regarding John-George's former employers. Hadn't they thrown her out of her home when her need was at its greatest?

But in the following weeks, even she revised her attitude,

111

for she began to appreciate that the village depended on the colliery for many of its needs. With a limited workforce, the mine could possibly close, threatening the whole community's way of life.

She was also distressed to see and hear of the many wounded casualties, appearing in the village and beyond.

'I hear Mr Nesham, our policeman's in hospital since he's come home,' Maggie was told by the local shopkeeper.

Maggie didn't want to ask for any details, she'd heard enough horrors from Allan. Besides it struck her that all she ever heard these days was bad news.

Allan agreed with her, when she brought it up at his next visit.

'Yes, I think many of the soldiers who've survived aren't too happy, many of them are waiting to be demobbed but it's taking an age and those that have been, are struggling to find work. Lloyd George has told us we've come back to a land fit for heroes but I don't see it at the moment. I'm thinking life is never going to be the same again for any of us.'

Maggie nodded in silent agreement .It was certainly true for her. She didn't admit it to Allan but initially she' d been jealous of the women in the village whose husbands had survived but now she was realising that it was not always the wonderful reunion the wives had longed for.

'My Johnny's come home a changed man,' an acquaintance had confided, 'and not for the better. We're even talking about divorce but I don't know whether it would be possible as neither of us have committed adultery, at least, I'm not aware that my husband's been with anyone else and I certainly haven't.'

Maggie had felt herself colouring up on hearing these words and rather than discuss it further, she'd made an excuse to go.

Now, staring back at Allan, as he sat in front of her, Maggie considered for a moment, how she truly felt about him. Was their friendship ever going to lead anywhere? Up to this point, she'd been relieved that he hadn't shown any interest in her. He'd never attempted to kiss her or even pay her any compliments. She'd been glad because she now feared intimacy, having no desire to create any more children ever again. But at the same time, she was beginning to question - had she lost her attractiveness? Usually men were more than eager to do her favours. Maybe, she told herself, Allan thought it inappropriate to have a relationship with his friend's wife. Or maybe he was just being a gentleman.

She was deep in thought when she was aware that Allan was relating yet more unpalatable news.

'There's also an outbreak of influenza,' he informed her,

'folks are calling it 'The Spanish Flu' because it's already killed millions in Spain. I hear some poor blighters who've survived the war have succumbed to it. People think it's become an epidemic because of all the crowds that gathered to celebrate the ending of the war; they've maybe all spread the infection.'

'Well, I'm so glad we never went to the celebrations then,' Maggie exclaimed.

'Yes,' Allan responded, 'apparently it attacks the fit and the healthy and it's so virulent it can kill you within the day. They say folks that get it turn purple and their lungs fill with a thick scarlet jelly that chokes them and... '

'Stop! Stop!' Maggie shouted, 'it's too awful to think about. Can't you tell me some happier news for a change?'

'Well yes, there's one good thing,' Allan went on, 'the government's chief medical officer has recommended that adults drink half a bottle of wine after dinner, as one way to try and prevent yourself succumbing to it.'

'I'm all for that,' Maggie replied, 'should we start right now?'

'Why not?' Allan agreed, 'Except we've no wine, have we?'

'No, that's right. Have you any other ideas?' she asked.

'They also suggest to ward off infection, that you wear a small gauze mask across the mouth,' he told her.

'Um, I don't think I'm all for that though! ' she replied, laughing.

Allan laughed too and then quite unexpectedly said,

'I agree, how can you kiss when you're wearing one of those?' and with that, he bent over and kissed her quite forcibly on the lips.

Maggie was taken aback. For the first time, he'd shown her some affection and she wasn't expecting it. Before she had time to respond, it was over. Allan appeared embarrassed and quickly made an excuse to leave.

After he'd gone, Maggie was puzzled. Why had he held back? Was he self-conscious? It wasn't normal for a man not to ask for more. But had she wanted him to take things further anyway? Perhaps, Maggie decided, now was the right time to put the past behind her and adopt a new attitude. Hadn't the greyness and misery of war taught her that it was best to live for the present? She'd heard that many were looking for new ways to find pleasure and that the cinema, music and dancing were all becoming more popular. Maybe she should find new ways of enjoying herself, even ways which might involve throwing 'caution to the wind,' even ways which might involve Allan. Not that she ever wanted any more children, they were most definitely off her agenda. She needed her freedom if she was to move forward and seize the day.

In the next few weeks, she allowed herself to become closer to him. He offered to support her financially and she agreed, knowing how much she needed a breadwinner. She accepted him calling on her every day and sharing meals together. So she wasn't totally surprised when Allan discussed marriage but she was shocked when he proposed:

'Why don't we get married on New Year's Day? I'm to be demobbed on January 7th and we can have a double celebration. It'll be a new beginning for us both.'

'But that's less than a month away, it gives us no time to prepare,' she argued.

Allan disagreed and tried hard to persuade her,

'What's there to prepare? It need only be a very small affair at the register office.'

Maggie didn't want to admit it but she needed more time to consider his proposal. In truth, she felt a certain reluctance and apprehension at the prospect of being his wife. She knew deep down that she didn't have any strong feelings of love for him. He wasn't particularly good looking; his hair was thinning, his mouth was hidden by a thick, greying bristly moustache and he was somewhat over weight - in fact he had the demeanour of a much older man than his forty-four years. He had also failed, so far, to show her any true affection - except for a few brief kisses - but perhaps he'd be more forthcoming if she did commit.

Yet on the plus side, she reminded herself that a marriage would provide her with the stability she so desperately needed. What had she to lose by marrying Allan? Nothing actually, for in reality, she had nothing without him - little money, no work, no family, in fact no life as such. Maybe he was her means of escape...

So despite her reservations, she agreed to become his wife and a very quiet wedding ceremony went ahead at the Durham Register Office on January 1st 1919. There were no friends or family there to celebrate, just two witnesses to make it legal. She hadn't even informed her family that she was marrying Allan, as in many ways she felt they'd disowned her, as she'd not seen them since she'd abandoned her children.

That evening, Allan appeared to be in no hurry to retire to bed. When he finally came to lay with her, there was certainly no seduction on his part. He took her quickly and with little emotion. It was all over before Maggie could respond. Where were the passion and the excitement that she craved? Immediately she felt misgivings over her decision to marry him.

Over the coming weeks, the two of them continued their daily lives in a monotonous routine. Allan working, often from dawn 'til dusk, to earn enough to support them and Maggie seeing to the household chores. Their time together was limited and though they still talked, Allan failed her physically. When they did come together, Maggie felt it was more from duty than any longing on his part. Maggie was grateful in one way as with little intimacy, she wouldn't be likely to conceive a child, at least that is what she hoped. Yet John-George, she recalled, had always needed and wanted her, too much at times, so this situation felt like another rejection in her life.

By early Spring Maggie was horrified to discover that she had been wrong in her assumptions. Even though their lovemaking had been very infrequent, she recognised the signs, especially the persistent sickness and knew she was carrying a child - for the sixth time. This was certainly not what she'd planned and the thought of the commitment involved made her extremely unhappy. Once more she felt herself failing to come to terms with the whole situation. A darkness descended which was an all too familiar feeling. She hated herself and began to despise her condition. Allan seemed delighted at the prospect of being a father again but he was soon to realise it wasn't what Maggie wanted .She became sullen and withdrawn. She wanted to close her mind to everything and just hide away. But nothing could be done to stop the inevitable.

* * * * *

'It's a boy!' the midwife exclaimed, as she held the baby up for Maggie to see, after an uneventful delivery. 'What are you going to name him?'

'My husband said he wanted to call the baby Ivan, if it was a boy, as he'd heard the name when he was abroad and liked it - it's Russian I think,' Maggie answered.

'Well it suits him with being born in January and with the weather being as cold as it is, it could be Russia outside!' she said smiling as she glanced out of the window and spotted the falling snow on the roof tops.

The midwife soon had the child cleaned and placed in Maggie's arms but despite him being a bonny child with dark skin and a mass of black hair, there was no instant bond - no surge of maternal love. She felt in some ways it wasn't fair to the five children she had abandoned that she was now about to take care of a new child. Besides, she conceded, this baby didn't deserve to have a mother who didn't want him and he would be better off with someone else.

'This is the son you wanted!' Maggie said rather emphatically as Allan walked into the bedroom to greet his child. Allan ignored the remark and moved to take the child from Maggie.

'He's just perfect' Allan said as he looked lovingly down onto his sleeping son, 'we are a real family now Maggie.'

Maggie was not so sure. She struggled on for the next three months. The days that followed were dreary and bleak and Allan, although adoring of Ivan, failed to understand how hard Maggie was finding life. He continued to work hard and for long hours, hence the time he spent with his 'new family' was limited. Even when they were in each other's company, it seemed to Maggie that they had nothing in common. She was still young enough to crave the more exciting way of life that she had vowed to have after the war. She didn't want to be trapped in a marriage that lacked passion and was unfulfilled. Allan had no concept of her emotional needs and showed little understanding of the demands a new baby made on a mother.

Her doubts about his suitability as a husband constantly surfaced and she rued the day she'd agreed to become his wife. She regretted even more having a sixth child but there wouldn't be a seventh. There was now no physical contact between them and affection was replaced by a constant tension, which was further compounded by Maggie's discovery that Allan had lied to her.

Tidying up one day, she'd found some of Allan's paper work and discovered he'd been dishonest. There in black and white was his year of birth - he'd been born in 1867.

What! Maggie worked out he wasn't forty-four as he'd stated on his wedding certificate but he'd been fifty-three when they'd married. That meant he was nineteen years older than she was - in fact old enough to be her father! Maggie challenged him that night.

'Why did you lie to me?' she screamed.

At first Allan said nothing but then he knew he would have to own up.

'I thought you wouldn't want me if you knew my true age,' he muttered.

'Too right!' she replied and then she stormed out of the house.

Maggie needed to escape. Always doubtful about her genuine feelings for Allan, now, more than ever, she questioned whether she actually wanted to continue with this relationship. Divorce she knew was inconceivable. Apart from not being able to afford it, she would have to prove adultery and she had no grounds to believe that he had been unfaithful. Allan was certainly a liar but not an adulterer. She could walk away, but if she did, she would need to consider what to do with Ivan? She decided she needed some time and space to consider her options.

Maggie returned to the house later that evening but ignored her husband as she took herself off to bed. That night, as she lay awake, her mind wouldn't settle. Instead she mulled over an idea that was forming in her mind. It was a shocking idea, she knew that, but then it was no different, indeed no worse than what she'd done before. Plus it was the only solution she could think of, as in reality, there were few alternatives.

The following day, after Allan had set off for work, she began to put her plan into action. First she fed Ivan and then dressed him in the best clothes she could find. She looked out and noticing it was a fine day, settled on a simple lightweight romper suit.

'You'll look lovely in this,' she told him, 'just like a proper boy.'

Next she placed a few items into her bag: a white muslin nappy, a bottle of milk and a change of baby clothes and then finally her purse. After putting on her wide brimmed hat and glancing in the mirror to check her appearance, she walked out of the door. She set out for the nearby village of Shincliffe, which was a journey she knew quite well. It was a hot summer morning but Maggie had no regard for the weather or for her surroundings. Her mind was focused elsewhere. She held on tightly to Ivan, hoping he wouldn't cry or cause a fuss. It was a two-mile journey and she feared Ivan would take some carrying but nothing was going to stop her.

After forty minutes, she arrived in the village and walked along the Back Lane until she came to the local shop. She was acquainted with the owner - Mrs Elizabeth Trotter, a lady she had known since the time she'd lived near South Shields. Mr Trotter had owned a fruit shop back then and whenever Maggie had called in as a child, she'd always seen Elizabeth his wife, surrounded by a brood of children. More recently, they'd met up again and despite the difference in their age, the two of them had gradually become good friends, with Maggie seeing Elizabeth as almost a mother substitute. Elizabeth was now a mature lady in her late forties but she still had several children living at home.

Maggie was pleased when she found the shop to be empty of customers, not wanting anyone to overhear their conversation.

'Hello Elizabeth,' Maggie began, still puffing from the exertion of holding Ivan, 'I'm so pleased to see you.'

'Are you alright Maggie?' Elizabeth asked kindly, as she

saw how flustered and red faced she appeared, 'you look totally hot and bothered.'

'I'll be alright once I get my breath back,' Maggie replied.

'And who's this?' questioned Elizabeth as she spotted Ivan.

'Didn't you hear, I've married again - back in January. Do you remember Allan, who came to find me after John-George died, well this is his child? He's called Ivan - he's six months old now,' Maggie answered in a rush, feeling a slight sense of shame over her revelations.

She knew many folk condemned her for the haste in which she'd remarried and then had a child but she hoped Elizabeth wouldn't be one of them.

Her friend was surprised but tried not to show it. Instead she reached out to Ivan and playfully tickled him under the chin.

'Why you're a bonny baby,' she cooed, as Ivan smiled up at her.

'How can I help you?' Elizabeth continued, as Maggie gave no indication of what she had come for.

Maggie hesitated and looked down at her son. She cleared her throat,

'I was just wondering if you would do me a favour? Would you mind looking after Ivan for me this morning, as I've an errand to do in Durham... but it shouldn't take me too long.'

Elizabeth smiled and her reply was just what Maggie expected,

'That's no problem, me dear, I'm happy to help, in fact me young 'uns will enjoy looking after him. Here pass him to me,' she continued.

'Thank you!' Hopefully I'll be back to collect him soon.' Maggie replied and apart from her ambiguity on timings, Elizabeth had no hint of her intentions.

With that, Maggie almost thrust Ivan into her arms, at such an impolite speed; it would be easy to imagine that she couldn't wait to be gone. Or was it just that she feared Mrs Trotter might change her mind and call her back?

'See you later,' was all Maggie said... and with that she was gone.

NINETEEN
Bowburn – 1920

Maggie felt she needed this break. It was a chance to work through her feelings. As she walked slowly back to Bowburn, she became totally enveloped in her own dark world - with thoughts deep inside her head - unstable thoughts that she recognised as those that had troubled her so often in her past. Her mind was exploding with both an agonising resentment for all that had befallen her and a deep self-loathing because of her selfish actions. She persecuted herself with endless questions and recriminations. Why had she been denied both her mother's love, after she'd died in childbirth and then her father's affection, after he'd abandoned her so cruelly? Why had John-George lost his life in the war, leaving her a widow with four fatherless children? Her kids hadn't deserved what she'd done to them but surely they were better off without her. But would they grow up to hate her? What sort of person was she, to allow herself to conceive a fifth child in such a shameful way? Had Oswald survived, she wondered, and if he had, would he always feel unloved and unwanted? Could she forgive herself for being so heartless? And didn't Ivan deserve to be cherished, too? What had she done leaving him with Mrs Trotter? It wasn't his fault that Allan and her weren't happy, he hadn't chosen to be born yet the thought of going back for him and returning to Allan was too unbearable.

She wandered along the narrow path, beside the road, in turmoil, oblivious to any passing people or transport. What was she to do? Yes, she acknowledged, Allan had come and offered her security at one of her lowest points in life but he'd disappointed her as a husband by not being more attentive - and he'd lied to her. Admittedly, she told herself, when Ivan arrived she had tried to be happy - to enjoy her latest child - for apart from his colouring, he had resembled her, in so many ways, especially with his laughing green eyes and his soft, wavy hair. He'd been an easy baby too, so contented and placid. But then why would she want Allan's child when she had turned her back on the children of John-George, the man she had only ever truly loved. She must have been kidding herself these last few months, believing that she had deep feelings for Allan and the thought of going back to him was abhorrent.

Feeling a rising sense of panic, she tried to calm herself and compose her thoughts. She must stop wasting all this needless energy on thinking, instead positive actions were required. First she must return home and collect some essential items, whilst Allan was not there.

As she entered the village, she hoped she wouldn't see anyone she knew. Most men would be at work and she realised all the mothers would be busily occupied in their backyards. It was a Monday - wash day and it was hectic filling the dolly tub with hot water, putting the clothes through the mangle and hanging the washing on the line. No time to be out on the street – at least that was what she was counting on.

On entering her silent house, Maggie rushed up the stairs and sat for a moment on the marital bed. What was she to do? Suddenly she jumped up, having spotted an old battered suitcase of Allan's that was lying on top of the wardrobe. She heaved it onto the bed and tried to think what she needed. Some warm clothes were essential, a few toiletries and one or two personal items, particularly her hairbrush and pins. Then she took her purse and filled it, with all the loose change she could find and put it in her handbag. At the last minute she also decided to take her birth certificate and placed it securely in the inner compartment of her bag for safe keeping. Finally she was ready.

She looked around for one last time and paused. There was just a moment of self -doubt but then she reminded herself that, what she was about to do, was for the best. As she left the house for the last time, she banged the door hard shut, as if marking the close of her present life. Then she hastened away with only a vague idea of where she was heading.

After what seemed an endless walk, Maggie found herself in Ferryhill near Tudhoe Colliery, almost eight miles south of Durham. There she managed to find lodgings at the home of a Mrs Ann Bell, living in Old Row. Mrs Bell, Maggie guessed must be at least ten years older than her but the two of them hit it off straight away. Mrs Bell didn't ask any prying questions which Maggie really appreciated. Conversely, Maggie paid a week's rent up front which Mrs Bell was grateful for. She showed Maggie into a single room with only the barest of essentials but Maggie felt it was adequate for her needs, after all she had very few possessions with her.

Maggie was sure she could now begin a new life away from people she knew and where she wouldn't be traced. She never imagined it was going to be easy but the reality was to be far harder than she imagined.

Over the following months, just going out shopping or

having any social life was greatly limited. She was constantly anxious in case anyone recognised her in the street. She even feared that Allan might come looking for her. Finances - or lack of them - was her biggest problem. Work was so hard to come by; her work options were limited apart from some basic nursing skills and she was restricted by how far she was able to travel. Plus the fact that she was still legally married was a hindrance as employers much preferred to employ single ladies. But did these factors have to be a hindrance to her plans?

Slowly, the beginnings of a new idea formed in her mind. There was a solution to these seemingly insurmountable problems but she realised it was quite far- sighted, even daring some would say. It was definitely going to be a challenge but Maggie was so despondent regarding her future, she had to be brave, she needed to be enterprising and she must definitely be resolute.

Why not, she asked herself, change her whole identity? If she were to alter her status and pose as a single lady, that might make her life so much easier. No one need ever know - at least not if she started a fresh existence, in a new location. It would have to be a distance from Durham. It would have to be far enough away for no one to recognise her. Yet at the same time, it would need to be a vibrant place where there would be both lodgings and employment readily available.

Now that she had decided, there was no time to waste. She collected together her few simple belongings in the well-worn suitcase, said goodbye to Mrs Bell and travelled to the railway station. A sense of anticipation grew in Maggie's mind but it was tinged with great sadness - this was a permanent goodbye to her past. She had accepted that her children were now in the care of others but this was, to her, a final act. This was forever. She knew beyond doubt that she would never see her six children again. It was very painful. Yet she couldn't see any alternative. Desperate times required desperate acts.

At the station, she felt her heart pounding. Where was she to go to start her new life? She walked onto the platform and spotted the train she was after. Its destination was a good place to go - she'd heard it was a lively city with a great variety of people. This was going to be where her new life would begin and she must face it with hope!

TWENTY
Manchester - Spring 1922

The journey to Manchester seemed to take forever and the darkness of night came well before the train arrived at the city's central station. Maggie had never felt so alone but there was no time for self-pity, instead, she must focus on her immediate need to find a place to sleep. The workhouse was never going to be an option. Just the thought of it made her feel uneasy.

After trudging the streets for a while and stopping various individuals to ask for help, she spotted a sign for a lodging house. It might take most of the money she had in her pocket but it was not something to concern her at that moment.

In fact Maggie was feeling quite heartened because, on leaving the railway station, she had spotted a poster, advertising work at a local mental hospital in Prestwich, just north west of the city. She would, she decided, investigate this opportunity in the morning, after a much-needed rest. She was absolutely exhausted - both mentally and physically.

Sleep didn't come very easily, though, that evening. Her mind would not rest. Before she embarked on her new life, she needed to be sure of her facts. Her new identity must be watertight. She would have to ensure that from now onwards she gave everyone the same details, otherwise her deception might be discovered.

First she needed a change of name - a name that was easy and memorable. That wasn't too difficult. Why not revert to Purvis? - her first married name - she'd never forget to answer to that. As for a Christian name, she immediately thought of her mother's. Yes - Mary Purvis - it sat well with her.

Next was the question of marital status. Would she admit to being married to Allan? Certainly not, telling everyone she was single was a far better option. That way there'd be no complications and gaining employment would be far easier.

Finally, she must consider the matter of her age. She would, she decided, change her year of birth from 1889 to 1896. This new age of twenty-seven, seemed ideal - mature enough to gain a good job but young enough to still be single. This would have to be a verbal lie for she realised her documentation wouldn't validate this claim.

With important decisions made, Maggie finally succumbed to slumber but she awoke early next morning and for a moment imagined herself back in Durham. Her thoughts turned to her children, wondering how they were faring, but these were only transient. She chided herself for her lack of self-control - she must focus on the future and not weigh herself down with any negative thoughts.

She forced herself out of bed and made the best of her appearance, with very limited resources. Her main task for that day was to find work and she needed to look and feel her best. She would begin by following up the opportunities outlined on the poster.

She was disappointed when she discovered it was raining outside, that wouldn't help improve her hairstyle but she was determined that it wasn't going to dampen her spirits. She strode down the street with a confident air, determined to live life to the full and not let anything get her down. She tried not to notice as her rather long skirt trailed in the puddles and her hands grew numb with the cold.

After some two hours on foot, she found herself approaching a stark Victorian hospital, surrounded by high brick walls and a very plain exterior, with column after column of identical sash windows. The building itself was foreboding rather than welcoming, with no gardens or pleasant walkway to the entrance, whilst the lights inside appeared as dismal and uninviting as the weather.

Maggie was feeling slightly nervous as she slowly walked up to the large, weathered door, yet a steely determination gripped her. This was her chance to start again - to look forward and forget the past. I'm not, she reminded herself, the person I was yesterday. She no longer exists. From today onwards I become a new, totally different woman. So I must stay calm and remember to provide all those deceitful details, I planned earlier.

'Have you travelled far?' enquired a smart lady, sitting upright behind a large, oak table.

'Yes, I've come from Spennymoor, near Durham,' Maggie replied without hesitation.

'That should serve you well - the powers that be like to take staff from afar, as it means there's little chance of them knowing the patients or their families.'

Maggie dared to allow a smile to cross her face. This was looking hopeful. She soon found herself in an interview room. The staff nurse was precise and officious, as she completed an application form.

' Name? '

' Mary Purvis.'

'Marital status? '

'Single.'

'Age and date of birth?'

'I'm twenty seven and I was born on June16th, 1896.'

The lies, so well rehearsed in her head, came effortlessly.

'Now, I need the names of three referees who'll vouch for your character,' the nurse continued.

Maggie coloured up - now this might be a problem. She thought quickly:

'Alright. First there's Mrs Bell - Ann Bell - my former landlady who lives at 15, Old Row, Tursdale Colliery, Ferryhill.'

Maggie assured herself that Mrs Bell knew nothing of her personal life, so she would never betray her, more likely she would vouch for her honesty and friendliness.

'Oh and Mr McIsaac can be my second one. He's from the post office in Front Street, Bowburn.'

He was a kindly man who had always acknowledged her when she went to collect her weekly pension, but he was renowned for his failing memory and often found it a problem to put names to faces .So that made him a good choice.

Maggie swallowed hard, 'Then... er... er... Mrs Marian Burns of Hunts Buildings, Pelton, will be my third one.'

What was she saying? She truly hoped this need for referees was just a formality, if the authorities happened to write to her stepmother, her lies might be disclosed. But then she was reassured by the knowledge that Marian wasn't known as a letter writer, so was hardly likely to provide a written reference anyway.

Next, Maggie found herself being accompanied down a long, narrow corridor to a small, dimly lit room where she was told to await their decision. She looked around at the highly polished but rather shabby furniture and the bare white distempered walls that seemed cold and clinical. She soon decided that the hospital was a sombre and sad place to be. The inmates, she'd been informed, were suffering from a whole range of mental illnesses, everything from fallen women to acute schizophrenics and apparently there were hundreds of them. In fact it was one of the largest asylums in the whole of Europe with patients, ranging in age, from young children to the elderly. Maggie was not phased though, for she had a certain empathy with these lost souls and felt she could perhaps make some difference to their empty existences. After all, hadn't she sometimes come close to the edge of normality herself?

Suddenly Maggie became aware of a voice breaking into her silent thoughts:

'You can start in a fortnight's time, working as a nursing attendant, but that's providing your references prove to be satisfactory. You'll be given a wage of twenty seven shillings and one penny a week plus there'll be lodgings available in the annexe, at the back of the hospital,'

Maggie, quietly confident that her first two referees at least wouldn't let her down was pleased and politely showed her appreciation for this offer, which she gladly accepted. So far things seemed to be going well. But, she reminded herself, for her plan to be fully successful, it was imperative she always answer to the name Mary, that she never talk of her former life and must pretend she's a twenty-seven year old, single lady - a lady who she now felt was ready for anything.

TWENTY-ONE
Manchester - Summer 1922

Within days of starting employment, 'Mary' had made friends with other staff members, many of whom were also newly appointed and in unfamiliar territory the same as her.

'Would you like to join us at the Mason's Arms tonight?' a fellow nurse asked, 'It's where a lot of the staff go to relax, after completing their shift.'

The nurse introduced herself:

'I'm Margaret White, I've worked here for the last six months but all my friends call me Meg'

'That's strange, my name...' Mary paused, smiling, stopping herself mid-sentence, realising she was about to revert back to her past identity.

'Strange that…' she repeated, collecting her thoughts, ' that my friend back home, her name was Margaret. My name is Mary - Mary Purvis.'

'Well maybe we could be friends, Mary,' Meg suggested tentatively and Mary nodded in agreement.

That evening, Mary found herself relaxing, enjoying some good company. The transition into 'Mary' was not posing any real problems, she just needed to stay focused and told herself not to accept too many offers of drink. Everyone seemed friendly and open and accepted her without question. She had, she decided, made the right decision to take this employment.

Over the following days, she quickly discovered the importance of spending time with friends, away from the stresses that came with her work. For nursing on the wards was, she realised, a far more onerous task than she had ever imagined. Not only was the job challenging, with many patients displaying extremes of behaviour; ranging from aggression to complete withdrawal, but the shifts were long and arduous. The standards of cleanliness were so high and the demands made by both her superiors and the patients were relentless.

Yet Mary discovered she had a natural affinity with the inmates and began to look forward to her shifts, despite these rigid expectations. She found it easy to befriend the less severe patients and even those with acute problems, who couldn't communicate, she endeavoured to give both time and respect.

'We admitted a new patient today. She was only a young girl and I feel so sorry for her,' Mary told her friend one evening.

'Why's that?' she questioned.

'Well she's in the hospital simply because she's been disappointed in love. It seems that it's traumatised her. But surely there are many girls who've experienced that.'

'Could that include you Mary?' her colleague enquired, noting how sympathetic she sounded.

'Yes, in a way,' Mary continued, 'although I wasn't exactly disappointed in love, more devastated, because my first love went missing in action during the war.'

Then, in order to deter more questions, she quickly asked,

'How about you?'

Meg lowered her eyes and put her fingers to her mouth, biting her nails, 'Actually, I was in love with a young soldier too, sadly he was killed right at the very end of the war.'

'That's so awful,' said Mary, placing her arm around her friend and giving her an encouraging hug.

Mary chided herself for darkening their mood. She suddenly stood up,

'Come on, we definitely need another drink, it'll be morning and work before we know it. And let's find something more cheerful to talk about, shall we!'

The next day, Mary awoke with a headache and was most disgruntled when she found out she'd been allocated to help out in the large laundry - her least favoured activity. Here, there was a damp, steamy atmosphere and a constant noise of machinery, which limited the chance of idle chatter. Backbreaking piles of fetid washing, which never went down, and continuous mounds of sheets, waiting to be ironed, were everywhere. But having some male company helped, particularly when Mary was on the receiving end of some rather desirable attention.

'And who might you be?' questioned a young Cockney lad, with a wicked smile and the most pleasant of faces. Mary guessed he was around her age – well the age she was pretending to be any way. She fed him similar lies to those she told everyone - name, Mary - status, single - then on a whim, she decided to reduce her age to twenty-five - but what did it matter? She was reinventing herself and who was to know the truth? Who would even care?

'And now tell me, who might you be?' Mary mimicked, her cheeks flushing.

'I'm Arthur Cannon,' he replied.

Mary quickly retorted, 'Well that's appropriate with you firing all these questions at me!'

Arthur laughed, loving the amusing way she had responded. He went on to explain that he was twenty-nine and that he'd served in India during the war. After he'd left the army, he'd responded to a poster advertising work opportunities at Prestwich Hospital.

Mary smiled, 'That's how I found my job too,' she informed him.

Mary was immediately smitten with Arthur but she was anxious not to show it. It was important not to look too keen or too desperate, it might put him off. Besides she was not sure if she was misreading his friendliness as something more. Arthur though, continued to lavish her with compliments throughout their shift - particularly remarking on her beautiful auburn hair.

'I love the colour Mary, it makes you stand out from the crowd,'

'Well it's all natural,' she assured him - 'I don't use dye like some girls do!'

'That means you're a natural beauty' he replied instantly and they both laughed.

Mary began to look forward to the times she had to work alongside him in the laundry. He was arousing feelings within her that she hadn't experienced for a long time. Arthur seemed so very different to Allan. Solid, dependable Allan had been rather boring and predictable, whereas fun loving, spontaneous Arthur was young, exciting and attractive. He had wonderful deep brown eyes, wavy black hair and a winning smile. Mary believed him to be the most attractive man she'd seen for a long while. She was besotted and was delighted when he asked if he could take her out:

'Do you fancy a walk out into the city on our next day off, Mary?' he asked.

'I've never been into Manchester, except to the railway station,' she informed him, 'so I'd love too, thank you.'

That evening, a very delighted Mary was eager to share her news with her friend.

'I envy you, Mary,' Meg said wistfully, realising she might be seeing rather less of her new companion, 'I think you've found someone who could be your soul mate. Be careful though, relationships between the staff aren't encouraged.'

Mary, being audacious, didn't particularly care what her superiors might think. She awaited their outing with eager anticipation and was frustrated that it was a whole week before they were both free.

On the Sunday morning, she agonised over what she should wear - even though she had very limited choice. She finally settled on a simple, pale blue shift dress, which although not entirely flattering to the figure, was quite fashionable and smart. She teamed it up with a navy cloche hat which she pulled down tight, hiding most of her forehead and revealing only a little of her lovely locks. She was pleased that she had resisted having her hair cut when she began her employment and hadn't adopted the new style bob, popular with so many girls. She had a final glance in the mirror and decided she looked quite elegant in her chosen outfit.

She had arranged to meet Arthur outside the hospital gates and when she arrived, exactly on time, he was already there. She was impressed that he looked equally smart and had obviously made an effort with his appearance. She immediately felt at ease and was grateful when he took charge, suggesting they took the tram into the city centre.

'I'll pay the fare,' he offered as he handed over four pence to the driver.

On their arrival, Arthur took Mary's arm and took her on a whirl wind tour of some of the local landmarks. She was entranced by everything and impressed at Arthur's local knowledge. Trafford Park, he explained was the world's first industrial park, created twelve years earlier. In Albert Square, he pointed out the famous Town Hall whose stonework was covered in soot. It made Mary think of all the grimy buildings back in County Durham but she had decided from the outset, not to make any reference to her former life, fearing it could lead to some awkward questions.

They continued on to Quay Street and there Mary was transfixed by the Opera House.

'This must be one of the most beautiful buildings I've ever seen,' she declared, as she stood enthralled by the façade, especially the huge horse drawn carriage within a semi-circular arch.

'I've always dreamt of being an actress and working in a theatre like this,' she told Arthur with great feeling.

'You'd certainly fit in well, you seem quite dramatic,' he retorted and they both giggled.

The day passed all too quickly and when it came to an end, Mary realised her feelings for Arthur were intensifying. She hoped for more from Arthur than his friendship but as yet there had been no physical contact. Mary decided he must be shy and inexperienced and in many ways this appealed to her. She'd known too many men who'd been forward and demanding. Admittedly Allan hadn't been one of them but then he'd been almost distant towards her, whereas Arthur was attentive and caring. She was relishing being treated like a lady and for now that was enough.

She was delighted when he suggested they meet up again, on their next free weekend. It seemed as if he was equally transfixed by her and knowing that made Mary very content.

The following Sunday, when they rendezvoused again, Arthur suggested they have a walk in Heaton Park, which Mary just loved.

'Apparently this is reputed to be the biggest park of its kind,' he informed her.

'Manchester must be quite famous,' she replied, 'don't we work in one of the biggest hospitals too?'

'Yes, that's right' Arthur affirmed before teasing her, 'And one day you might be famous for being the best actress!'

'Maybe not,' she sniggered with amusement, 'but you never know, I could be famous for something or other, one day!'

The pair of them continued to exchange light hearted banter throughout the day. They both felt totally at ease and after enjoying a wonderful, carefree time, getting to know each other better, neither of them wanted it to come to an end.

'Come back to my room,' Mary whispered as they entered the hospital grounds.

Arthur hesitated, knowing he would be in serious trouble if caught in female quarters.

'It's Sunday evening, there's no-one about, besides, it's dark, you'll not be seen,' she reassured him.

Once safely inside, Mary encouraged Arthur to relax. He glanced around the spartan room, which he decided was a mirror image of his own, back in the adjoining male dormitory. He sat himself down in the only armchair, squashed in between the narrow bed and a simple cupboard, which acted as both a wardrobe and a dressing table. Arthur watched intently as Mary kicked off her shoes, pleased to be free of their discomfort. He studied her admiringly as she took off her coat and carefully removed her hat. After placing them on the hooks, behind the door, his eyes continued to follow her as she went over to the mirror, which was hanging from an old nail, above a small sink with a single tap. One by one, she slowly removed the metal grips, that fastened up her hair, allowing her auburn locks to tumble, almost to waistline. Arthur was entranced. Suddenly Mary was aware that he was right behind her.

'I just love your hair, please promise me you'll never cut it,' he said as he gently stroked the full length of it.

'I promise' Mary replied, 'but only if you promise…'

Her voice trailed off as he spun her round and leant over to kiss her. The passion of it took her by surprise, for she felt sure he was inexperienced.

'Who taught you to kiss like that?'

Arthur didn't answer but simply kissed her again, this time more tenderly.

'You said earlier you wanted to see more of me,' she said coyly, as she began to undo the buttons of her dress, 'Did you really mean that?

Arthur quickly placed his hand on top of hers, he was smiling as he spoke.

'No Mary, what I meant is that I've fallen in love with you and I want to see you and be with you whenever I can.'

Mary's face flushed as a wave of emotion overwhelmed her. This man, this gentleman, had just declared his love for her. He didn't want to take advantage of her like other men before him. This reassurance meant everything. At that moment, all her sad and difficult memories evaporated and she was desperate to respond.

'Arthur Cannon, I love you too,' she whispered. Then she gently took his hand away, so she could continue undressing...

From that day onwards, the pair endeavoured to meet at every opportunity. Mary's new found happiness was evident to everyone as she rediscovered that life could be fun and pleasurable despite the daily grind of trying to earn a decent living. Her only fear was wondering if her contentment would last, for she knew, only too well, that life didn't always go to plan.

TWENTY-TWO
Manchester - Winter 1922

Before long, familiar symptoms surfaced, signs Mary recognised but ones she certainly didn't want to face. The nausea she suffered each morning and the sensitivity of her breasts meant just one thing. A slight feeling of panic gripped her, for having a child, might well spoil everything. Also, she reminded herself, she must be extremely careful not to indicate these were feelings she'd experienced before.

'I think I might be carrying your child,' she volunteered to Arthur, on their next meeting, as yet again the wave of sickness caused her to complain of dizziness and fatigue.

Arthur was quiet at first and she questioned the nature of his true feelings. Had she been fooled again into thinking a man genuinely loved her? Had she just been taken advantage of once more? Did he not like her any longer?

But if she'd known Arthur better, she would have realised his silence was simply him thinking and planning in his mind the best way forward. He was so calm and not a man to over react.

'Let's get married then, Mary,' he said - nothing else - but spoken with extreme composure and a sincerity that implied he wasn't fooling around.

'Married!' Mary hesitated, repeating the words, allowing them to sink in. She hadn't given any prior thought to what her reaction might or should be over such a proposal. Her feelings for Arthur were real - he had attracted her right from that first meeting but marriage, that was rather a different proposition. She knew deep down, she wasn't free to marry him. Although she had a new identity, including a new name, the truth was she was still married to Allan and there was no escaping it. This meant if she married Arthur illegally, she would become a bigamist, which she'd heard was a criminal offence, even punishable by imprisonment. But Mary smiled at her foolish thoughts - this was only true if you were found out. Hadn't she covered her tracks sufficiently for no one to ever discover her lies? Hadn't she also promised herself that with her new life, she would seize the moment, for she knew only too well that happiness was transient and could so quickly be lost?

'Yes, I'd love to be married,' Mary heard herself saying, 'I can't wait!'

'Let's see how soon we can arrange it then,' Arthur replied.

'Arthur's proposed and we're getting married as soon as possible,' Mary told her friend the following morning.

'As soon as possible,' Meg repeated. 'You're not in the family way, are you?

Mary blushed. 'Yes I am, but please don't tell anyone at the moment. I'd rather wait until we're married before I disclose it.'

'That's fine - I can keep a secret,' she promised.

'You're a good friend, thank you,' Mary continued, 'and I was hoping you could do me another favour. We will need two witnesses at the register office, Arthur is asking his mate, Fred Thompson and I wondered if you'd be the other one?'

Meg agreed immediately, 'I'd love to be.'

The following month, on a Wednesday afternoon, the four friends took time off work and went to the Register Office in Prestwich. It was a brief ceremony, completed in a matter of minutes but Mary was glad that no one else was present. For afterwards, Mr Worsarck, the Registrar, started asking awkward questions as he completed the marriage certificate:

No problem with the date - March 21st 1923.

But then he wanted the bride's details:

'Name?'

'Mary Purvis.'

'Age?'

'Twenty-five.'

'Marital status?'

'Single.'

'Father's name?'

'John Purvis.'

Mary appeared composed but inside her heart was thumping. She felt increasingly uncomfortable as she relayed lie after lie. This was an official document he was completing with legal implications. For the first time she had a conscience and the guilt she felt was hard to suppress.

'Let's go and have a celebratory drink,' Fred suggested afterwards, having no idea of the state of Mary's mind.

'That's a good idea but let's not tell anyone the reason for it, we don't want Mary losing her employment just yet,' Arthur insisted.

Mary went along with their plan, thinking a drink might help settle her, not for a moment considering its effect on the baby.

Over the following weeks, a wide range of emotions jostled inside her head. She was thrilled when Arthur found a small house to rent in the Stand Farm area of Manchester. She was delighted at her good fortune to have both a new home and a loving relationship with a kind and thoughtful man. But then there were occasions when she was plagued by anxiety over her dishonesty. She wasn't proud of the fact she'd deceived Arthur and it was a strain to maintain the pretence. As the weeks passed and summer arrived, she was exhausted after every shift. This was of course her seventh pregnancy but having to pretend it was her first was not easy. As she grew in size, her struggle to stay silent and hide her condition at work became more difficult.

Her mind wandered to past times and thoughts of her children surfaced. Realising it did her no good, she vowed to try and focus resolutely on this birth. Childbirth had never been a pleasant experience but at least this time she knew she wanted the baby, unlike her previous two.

Arthur was proving to be a caring and devoted husband and the love between them was indisputable. He helped her when chores became arduous and he supported her when the tiredness overwhelmed her. He had no indication of course regarding the turmoil of thoughts racing around her mind. What did he know of the thoughts and feelings of a pregnant woman? On the days her temper surfaced and she shouted at him in exasperation, he attributed it to her 'condition'. When she turned her back on him at night, he consoled himself with the thought that there would be many other days and nights to make love in the future. And as he watched as his wife's midriff expanded and the weight piled on, he assured her she was still attractive to him. He had no notion that Mary's pregnancy was a re-occurring event.

It was on a Saturday morning, in mid September 1923, Mary called out, knowing her husband was about to set off for his early morning shift:

'I think the baby's coming, Arthur! Please, don't leave me!'

Arthur, maintaining his usual calm demeanour, went off to summon the help of the local midwife. She duly arrived and was quite shocked at how far Mary had progressed.

'For your first child, this baby's not taking long!' she commented.

With that, Mary gave a final push and the baby was soon announced as 'A boy!'

Mary smiled, knowing that this was what she had expected. Out of her seven confinements, only once had she given birth to a girl.

'Shall we call him Thomas?' Arthur suggested as he proudly held his first born son.

Mary liked that idea for her thoughts turned back to those

many years ago, when she had watched her first delivery. The young miner's wife, Isabella, had called her baby Thomas and she'd remembered his name ever since.

'Thomas Arthur would be ideal,' Mary replied, 'as he looks just like you.'

He had a covering of dark brown hair with no hint of auburn at all. Mary felt a rush of love - this she felt was the new beginning she so desired. From the moment she held him, she knew the past was behind her and nobody was even aware of it. Maybe now she could enjoy a proper family life, happy in the knowledge that her future was secure, even though it had meant giving up the job at the hospital, which she had enjoyed so much.

TWENTY-THREE
Durham - 1918-1923

Back in Durham however, there were six children born to Margaret who were no longer experiencing their mother's love. Not for them the warmth of a father and mother's attention, or the joy of a happy family life.

Jacob, her eldest, was in turmoil, trying to come to terms with just exactly what his mother had subjected him to.

'What happened to you, son? Who are your parents and where have you been living? How come you found yourself on the street?'

The questions kept coming and were beginning to really irritate him. After a few days of living by himself on the street, the authorities had picked him up, after they had found him wandering alone, tired and hungry. Now an older man and a lady were trying to discover his real identity, in the faint hope of reuniting him with his family. Jacob, however, had no desire to return to his errant mother, so he decided to lie.

'Me da's been killed fighting in the war and then me mother died - must have been a broken heart, I reckon,' was all he would tell them.

'Then we'll send you off to Gilesgate, to the Durham Poor law Institution Boy's Home,' the man announced.

Jacob thought he knew exactly what that meant. To him, just the mention of Gilesgate made him think of the workhouse. His mother had referred to it previously, when they'd first been evicted from their miner's home. It was the place she'd feared above all else, for to enter it was considered shameful plus it had a reputation for harshness. There was even a suggestion that once you went inside its walls, you rarely came out.

Jacob felt his body tremble and his stomach knot. How could his mother have done this to him? Did she no longer love him? Why had none of her family been prepared to take him in, when they'd willingly offered their homes to his brothers and sister?

Jacob stared sullenly at the couple and remained silent. He didn't like the feeling of being classed as a 'waif and stray' and he certainly didn't want to be forced to do what they were suggesting.

'We'll try to see it as a temporary measure,' the man said, almost reading Jacob's thoughts, 'it would be good to find you a foster home eventually.'

Jacob rallied somewhat on hearing this and he begrudgingly accompanied them, as they showed him his new 'home'. It was almost as bleak as he expected and he immediately made up his mind that he wasn't going to like it. His negative attitude was so intense, that at first, he found solace in nothing and no one. He was full of so much hurt and hatred for his mother that it created a deep resentment which spilled over into angry outbursts. The other children soon learnt that he wasn't to be crossed. Over the coming weeks he found some release from the fury that raged inside him, when he was taught to play rugby. Finding something he was good at gave him some self-esteem and also some recognition from the other boys. He was still determined though to break free from what he almost classed as his captivity.

I'll go off down south, away from here, when I'm old enough, he told himself, and I'll join the army as soon as I can and become a soldier, like me da.

He was sad to think that it would mean saying goodbye, maybe forever, to his siblings, particularly his younger sister Ann because he'd always felt quite protective of her, but he was certain she would be settled now and would always be well looked after, by their grandparents.

And in some ways, he thought correctly. Ann had settled down with Jacob and Marian for she'd realised, right from the start, that she had little choice other than to be compliant and accept what had happened. Usually ebullient and full of life, recent events had numbed her, causing her to become withdrawn and pensive. The truth was hard to bear. Her father was dead - she accepted that for she had only the vaguest of memories of him. But being separated from her three brothers, not knowing if she would ever meet up with them again was hard to come to terms with. She clung to the hope that her mother would be back to collect her in the near future and they'd be reunited as a family.

'Is mother coming back for me soon?' she asked her grandfather, desperate to understand what was going on.

'What's that - you've hurt you back?' Jacob said, barely picking up any of what she said.

'Oh granddad,' Ann sighed, feeling frustrated by his deafness, 'you never hear anything these days,' and then she repeated the question again, almost shouting in his ear.

He was at a loss to know how to reply.

'I've not heard from your mother for a while, Ann,' was all he would say, not wishing to give her any false hope.

Later that evening, he discussed the issue with Marian. Both of them were convinced that Maggie would not be returning. They'd seen nothing of her for many weeks and they'd heard that John-George and Roland had been abandoned too. They talked over different possibilities and Jacob was adamant that Ann didn't need to hear the truth. He felt it would be too upsetting to tell her that her own mother didn't want her. He had an alternative solution…

'I'm sorry to tell you that your mother caught the Spanish flu and she's died,' he informed Ann rather insensitively, later that week.

Ann believed him but it took a lot of accepting. For many days she felt an intense inner sadness. She had enjoyed a loving relationship with her mother, especially as she had been slightly favoured as the only girl but now her mother was dead and that must mean she was an orphan. She found that so hard to deal with. Instead of talking about it, she filed it away into the deepest recesses of her mind, deciding that she never wanted to confront it, not then or at any time in the future.

Jacob and Marian tried in their own way to support her, in the following days but at sixty-four and fifty-two respectively, they found it extremely hard. Their own children were now grown up and they struggled to find enough energy or enthusiasm to cope with the demands of a young girl. They sent Ann to school in Pelton and fortunately, it was there that she began to find solace.

Making friends with the other children provided her with some of the companionship that she was missing from her brothers. She particularly enjoyed spending time with the local butcher's daughter, Edith Lough

'When we're older let's leave Durham,' she announced to Edith one day, 'I'd really like to go to a seaside town - somewhere along the east coast would be good. It should be so much better than this place.'

Edith agreed and the two of them promised each other to carry out their plan as soon as they were adults.

Ann knew it would mean cutting off links with her family but she was determined to make a fresh start as soon as she was old enough to find employment. She hoped though that she wouldn't lose permanent touch with her younger brothers. At the moment, she was aware they were at her aunt's house and hoped that she'd still be able to see them when opportunity allowed.

Roland and John-George felt they were somewhat more fortunate than their older sister, in that they had been abandoned together. They had begun to settle with Margaret's sister-in-law Jenny and her husband Arthur, who were still relatively young.

138

They were expected to help with chores but they were used to that and they enjoyed regular meals and a warm comfortable bed to sleep in every night - something they hadn't experienced for quite a while. Even though they didn't see a lot of Uncle Arthur, they appreciated when he did find time to give them attention and they felt secure knowing their aunt was there to take care of them.

One evening, several months after their arrival, Roland overheard Arthur talking to his wife in a hushed tone. He strained to catch all of the conversation but he heard enough to unsettle him, not that he fully understood its implications.

'I've been told the mine's closing next week, I shall have to look for alternative employment and I reckon my best chance is to go down to London.'

'But Arthur, how will we manage with the boys? Won't it be too expensive to find lodgings to accommodate the four of us?' Jenny replied.

'I've been thinking about that,' Arthur replied, 'and I don't think we'll be able to take the boys with us, it's just won't be practical.'

'But Arthur, I promised Maggie that I'd look after her two boys,' insisted Jenny.

'And didn't she promise us that she'd be back to collect them when her circumstances improved,' he countered, 'and it never happened, did it.'

Tears began to run down Jenny's face - the awful realisation dawned on her that maybe Arthur was right; she knew Maggie wasn't ever going to have them back and with a move imminent, it seemed they had little alternative but to leave the boys behind.

'So, so …What's to become of them?' Jenny continued, barely able to get the words out in between her sobs, 'they're only five and seven, they need a mother's love.'

'I guess it'll have to be the orphanage,' Arthur said bluntly but inside he was feeling almost as guilty as Jenny.

'Well you can tell them,' Jenny insisted as she walked off in a distressed state.

The following evening, Arthur took the two boys aside and held them close. His voice cracked as he spoke, 'I think you both know that the mine where I work is closing down. I've managed to secure some new work down south but I'm sorry to tell you, we'll not be able to take you with us.'

The boys stayed quiet for what seemed an age, causing Arthur to wonder if they'd understood. Roland was first to break the silence.

'So, what's to become of us?' he asked in his typically

sensible manner.

'We're going to send you to a Boy's Home in Durham,' Jenny interrupted, 'but you'll stay together,' she added hoping to soften the blow.

'Don't want to go,' John-George remarked, although in truth he had no idea where he was being sent or what it would be like.

Roland folded his arm around his brother, 'I'll look after you,' he promised.

The final parting came a few days later. It was traumatic for all of them.

Both boys clung to their Aunt Jenny, 'I promise to write to you,' she said softly as she dabbed her handkerchief to her eyes. 'Remember how much we love you and be good boys to make us…' but then she lost her composure completely and had to turn away. Arthur, feeling choked himself, decided the best course of action was not to prolong their goodbyes.

'Time to go,' he insisted and with a last embrace, they were gone.

The two boys were then escorted down a long corridor by a rather formal lady, dressed in what the boys assumed was nurses' attire and taken to their dormitory. It seemed very large with its uniform rows of single beds, each with a crisp, white sheet and a grey wool blanket, plus a small side locker. There was a distinct chill in the air and its eerie silence suddenly made the place seem very foreboding. Roland and John-George were very grateful to be allocated beds next to each other and were then informed that it was lights out at seven, every evening.

The brothers were then shown into another vast reception room. The noise of children's chatter reverberated around them. John, being particularly shy, clung to his brother for security. Roland instinctively took hold of his brother's hand and although he didn't want to admit it, he too felt rather intimidated by the overwhelming number of children, all deemed by the authorities to be 'waifs or strays'.

By the end of the day, both boys were feeling completely lost. They were wary of everyone and they were missing the comforts of home. Just going into the dining hall that evening was an ordeal. Where should they sit? They walked in together, looking around, trying to ascertain what they should do. Roland suddenly gasped in total shock. For there, sitting at one of the large trestle tables was their brother Jacob. He was equally taken a back. They sat together and shared their stories and all three of them found support and encouragement in each other. They just wished their sister Ann could be there too, although they all acknowledged she was better off where she was. Jacob, although never close to his brothers, felt his low spirits lift. He no longer felt so isolated although he did wonder if their reunion might be temporary.

'You'll be enrolled in Blue Coats School, as soon as possible,' Jacob informed them, 'so we'll be able to meet up there during the day, as well as here each evening.'

Roland and John-George were delighted but then Jacob, realising he might be giving them a false sense of security, added, 'But I'm to be sent to a foster home in the future, so I'm not sure how long we'll be together.'

* * * * *

Roland and John-George didn't realise that plans were soon to be discussed, hoping to find them a new family. Their plight came to the attention of the British Legion, formed in 1921, with the aim of helping the families of veterans, such as theirs, whose parent had been killed or injured in the war. They set out to find the boys a suitable foster family.

Several months later, the boys, now ten and eight, were shocked when two ladies summoned them from their beds, in the early hours of the morning, and ordered them to dress quickly:

'You're going on a train ride,' they were told.

Neither of the boys had ever been on a train before and the sheer excitement of it temporarily erased their sadness at leaving behind their brother. The train sped on, with a brief stop at Crewe station, and finally completed its journey in the city of Bath, in the county of Somerset.

Roland and John-George needed little encouragement to alight from their carriage as they were more than eager to see this 'new country' for themselves.

When Roland left the station and saw - for the first time in his life - clean, tree-lined streets and wide open spaces, he declared.

'I think I've died and gone to heaven!'

The two ladies who had accompanied them smiled and informed the boys that they were about to meet Mr and Mrs Quick - their new 'mother and father'. Roland and John, as he now opted to be called, didn't know what to think but followed willingly. They were led along the quiet streets, arriving at an impressive terraced house, on the northern edge of the city, on Lower Bristol Road. A smart, middle-aged woman opened the door and she greeted the two children warmly, urging them to go inside.

She introduced them to her husband, Albert, who was a monument sculptor and explained that from now on they were going to look after Roland and John.

The two boys were stunned by this turn of events and faced

it with a mixture of emotions. John still hadn't accepted his separation from his mother. Despite abandoning him, he still held her in high esteem, putting her on his self-made pedestal. He needed space and time to come to terms with his changed circumstances. But Roland had real hope that this would be the chance of a new, happier life for them both and he was more than ready to embrace it.

'We'll be alright,' he said trying to reassure John, 'as long as we stick together,' and John was more than happy to believe him.

In Durham, Jacob was found a caring foster family, within the local area, but it didn't bring him the happiness that he longed for. He was most unwilling to be given orders by people he didn't even know, let alone care about. For despite their attempts to show him affection and understanding he felt a total indifference towards them. He had always displayed a rebellious streak, ever since his da had gone off to fight, but now it resurfaced, becoming almost out of control. It also gave him a steely edge- an inner strength – which made him determined to stand up for himself and be totally independent. So he made up his mind to run away. Now, he felt was the ideal time to pursue his dreams and fend for himself.

Oswald didn't have a choice whether to hate or love his mother as he wasn't even aware he had a mother. Institutionalised since Maggie had left him on the workhouse steps, all he had ever known was a sea of faces - some adults, many children, who came and went on a frequent, daily basis. He had no experience of being truly loved and cared for, sharing his day to day existence with many other 'unfortunates'. In the record books he had simply been recorded as the child who was 'found deserted.'

As a young toddler, he was weak and sickly and he failed to thrive. Concern grew for his mental capacity as he seemed to be slow at learning. It wasn't too long before he was labelled as 'mentally defective' and the medical officer decided that sometime in the future he would need to be transferred to a school for mentally defective children.

Ivan was not so unfortunate. He too had never known his mother but at least he had a mother substitute in Mrs Trotter.

At first, after Maggie's disappearance, Allan was concerned she'd come to some harm. Had she been involved in an accident? He anxiously awaited news, expecting to learn she'd either been taken to hospital or worse still that she'd lost her life. It was surely the only possible reason behind her vanishing act. Yet in the back of his mind, there was a nagging doubt, being fully aware that she had abandoned five children in the past. After several days, when he'd heard nothing, he had to conclude that his doubts were correct and that she'd gone out of her own choice, leaving him to look after their child on his own.

'I'd like to adopt Ivan' Mrs Trotter offered, when she heard of Allan's predicament though he didn't want to accept.

'Thank you for your kind offer but I really want to bring him up myself,' he told her. 'But I would appreciate it, if we could come to a financial arrangement. How about if you look after him during the day and I'll pick him up after work?' he suggested.

Mrs Trotter agreed, she loved children and she was happy to help. She felt genuine compassion for both the child and his father and was barely able to understand how any woman could leave her child, especially deserting him in such a deceitful way. She'd known many hard times in her own life, having a large family of nine to her husband who was a trades union clerk, but she'd had to cope. She was quite incensed that Maggie, who she'd considered to be a genuine friend could have done such a cruel thing and now she was determined to make amends and try and give Ivan the love he deserved.

Allan was equally resolute. He was shocked at what Maggie had done. He knew things weren't quite right between them but he found it hard to forgive her for this sudden and unexpected act of callousness in deserting him and abandoning their young son. To leave Ivan in the care of Mrs Trotter, with no intention of returning, was beyond his comprehension. He'd always known Maggie had had a love of 'the bright lights' and sought more excitement than what life gave her but he never expected her to pursue these dreams.

TWENTY-FOUR
Manchester – 1925/6

Back in Manchester, with a strong, loving husband to support her, Mary thrived. She'd never shirked hard work and was at her best when baking, keeping a tidy home and caring for her son and husband. Whenever Arthur returned from his shifts, even if it was very early in the morning, she always made it a priority to care for his needs. She had a hot meal waiting, some fresh, clean clothes laid out for him and always ensured there was plenty of hot water in the boiler for his ablutions. It was a pattern she'd learnt from childhood, first when her own father Jacob had returned from the pit and then watching her sister Nancy play the dutiful and loving wife to William and latterly to her first husband John-George.

Despite her inevitable weariness, Mary was very keen to maintain her appearance. This, she felt, was especially important if she wanted to keep up the pretence that she was nine years younger than her true age. She worked hard on keeping her figure trim, even if it meant the discomfort of a steel based corset to pinch in her waist. She took pride in her long, striking hair, which had so attracted Arthur on their first meeting. She would braid it carefully into two plaits, which she then coiled around her ears, framing her face. She was especially pleased when Arthur noticed her efforts and truly appreciated being told how much she was loved and cherished. She greatly enjoyed the warmth and intimacy that they shared.

Within eighteen months she wasn't at all surprised to discover she was expecting a second child.

'I'm sure I'm having another baby Arthur and I reckon it will be due around Christmas.'

Arthur acted in his usual calm and restrained way, not showing too much emotion but Mary knew how pleased he was. But no one could have been more delighted than Mary, when on 31st December 1926, she gave birth to a girl, whom they named Rosa. Calling her Rosa was Mary's idea - it was linked to her past for she'd walked down Rosa Street in Spennymoor so many times and always thought it would be a pretty name for a girl.

Having Rosa fulfilled Mary's deepest desire. She had longed for another daughter, remembering the close relationship she had had with Ann, plus there was an added benefit:

'Why, Arthur, our family is complete, now that we have a boy and a girl,'

In truth Mary couldn't face further confinements although she was never able to verbalise such thoughts to Arthur. But how to avoid more children was an on-going problem, although she had heard that there were new ways to prevent conceiving; there was talk of someone called Marie Stopes who was saying it was alright to limit your family and that there were ways round it. To Mary this was revolutionary, the freedom to have sexual pleasure without the fear of conception was almost unbelievable. She must, she told herself, make further enquiries...

The months that followed were exhausting and demanding but Mary was slowly evolving as a new woman. The depression, that had haunted most of her adult life, was less evident, as she enjoyed being married to Arthur and relaxed into being a mother of two. The one on-going problem she had to face, was the question of money or rather the lack of it. Despite working for long, endless hours at Prestwich Hospital, Arthur was poorly paid, making life a permanent financial struggle. So, Mary was determined to make her own contribution to supplement the family income, with cleaning jobs for the neighbours. She also earned a little extra, by offering to light fires for Jewish families on a Saturday, as their beliefs dictated that they must not do any manual work on the Sabbath day. As Arthur worked night shifts and so slept during the day, Rosa and Thomas had to tag along with their mother but they were generally no trouble.

By now the family had moved to a three bedroom, terraced house in Egmont Street, Cheetham Hill that was north of the city. Here the rows of terraced houses with their rudimentary toilets and their back to back yards were not dissimilar to her earlier miner's homes back in Durham. But this time they had the luxury of a bathroom. Mary prided herself on keeping everywhere spotless and tidy. She had developed her housekeeping skills when taking care of John-George in their first home that she'd been so proud of - not that she ever mentioned Bowburn. In fact she'd found it easier than she thought possible to block out her former life.

As winter approached, Mary began to feel off colour and she lost her energy and enthusiasm for her domestic chores. The children seemed to be more demanding than usual and daily tasks became a real effort. Even Arthur noticed she had slowed down and become more short-tempered than normal. She'd always been quite emotional but now tears seemed to be a regular occurrence.

'What's wrong Mary?' Arthur asked after yet another bout of crying.

'What's wrong!' Mary repeated in exasperation, 'what's wrong is that I'm expecting again.'

Arthur couldn't understand why Mary was so upset at this news. He recognised there was an issue with a third child to support, having to make their limited budget stretch even further, but he assured Mary that they'd manage, especially if he could get extra shifts at the hospital.

'It's not just a question of money Arthur, it's hard going through another pregnancy at… at my age.

She stopped herself, just in time from revealing that she was almost forty.

'Don't make yourself old before your time,' Arthur said encouragingly.

'Yes but it's not like I have any family around to help me,' Mary continued.

Arthur tried to understand her reluctance to have a third child but found it difficult, for he was pleased with the idea of having another baby in the house, as he loved children.

'You'll cope, you always do,' he said reassuringly.

The truth was he had no idea just how well she had coped in the past, bearing in mind Tom and Rosa were actually her seventh and eighth children.

Over the following months, Mary tried to come to terms with the idea of having a ninth baby. Some days she found it acceptable, especially knowing how happy it made Arthur, but on the days when she felt unwell, her mood became self-pitying and melancholic.

She promised herself that this must be the last baby, even if it meant turning down Arthur's advances in the future. She was convinced her body just couldn't survive another pregnancy. She called to mind her own mother who'd died after her eighth birth and she could now identify with her completely .She was adamant that she wasn't going to end her days in the same way. If only she could share these thoughts with Arthur...

'Arthur! Arthur! I'm sure the baby's coming,' Mary shouted late one evening in May.

'Are you sure?' he exclaimed, 'isn't it too early?'

'I can't help it, if the baby wants to come now, I can't stop it!' Mary replied impatiently, whilst gripping her stomach and gasping with the pain.

'Lay down, lay down on the bed!' Arthur ordered, 'I'll run and fetch some help.'

Mary was well-advanced in labour by the time Arthur

returned with the midwife.

'The birth's imminent,' the midwife announced as she quickly assessed Mary's progress.

Mary was showing signs of exhaustion and the midwife watched in horror as she struggled to deliver the baby.

The final stage seemed to take such an age that she feared for the life of both the mother and the child. When the baby finally arrived, it was alive but only barely. Mary was too weak to speak and the midwife was out of her depth. She insisted that a doctor be called.

The doctor immediately ordered complete bed rest for Mary but his main concern was for the child. The baby, a boy whom they decided to call William, was struggling with every breath.

'I think he may be too under developed to survive,' the doctor warned them, 'there's little to be done for him.'

Within a few hours, William's breathing deteriorated further, his little chest heaved as he fought to inhale. Mary and Arthur looked on helplessly as slowly and painfully, he gave up his fight for life.

Arthur and Mary were inconsolable. Arthur was distraught at losing his second son, who apart from being so small, had looked so perfect. Mary was tormented, thinking that all those times she had wished she wasn't having a child had now become a self-fulfilling prophecy. Was this punishment for all her past misdemeanours? How she ached to hold her precious child but his life had been so quickly extinguished.

Fortunately Tom and Rosa were too young to be aware of their parent's heartache but it was very hard for Mary to stay focused on them. She desperately wanted to hide away and grieve all by herself but she forced herself to carry on. Hadn't she always? Her life had seemed to be a constant battle, with endless setbacks, which she'd had to overcome. At least this time she had Arthur to share her grief and for that, she was grateful.

It took them both a long time before they could come to terms with their loss. It was yet one more thing that Mary filed away and tried to blot out, for it was the only way she had learnt to survive.

TWENTY-FIVE
Eleven years later, Manchester – 1939

In the summer of 1939, rumours were surfacing that yet another war with Germany was imminent. The British Prime Minister, Neville Chamberlain, had tried to avoid conflict but it seemed Adolf Hitler had every intention of putting his plans, to conquer Europe, into action. His troops invaded Poland on September 1st, so two days later, the government announced Britain was at war. Immediately, an Act of Parliament was passed, which imposed conscription on all males between eighteen and forty-one.

On hearing this news, Mary was full of trepidation, reflecting on the potential disaster such a conflict could bring upon her family. Surely she had known enough suffering and loss in her life already, she couldn't contemplate a repeat of what she had experienced twenty-two years earlier. Nobody, in her present family, knew of the immense heartache the death of her first husband had caused but it, as well as more recent tragedies, were utmost in her own mind.

'I'm so pleased Arthur that you're too old, at forty seven, to be conscripted,' she said to her husband that evening, 'besides, you did your duty in the Great War.'

'I feel sorry for those lads whose age means they have to go and fight for a second time,' Arthur replied.

Mary agreed but her concerns were closer to home.

'I'm really worried about Tom, it won't be that long before he's the right age to be called up.'

'Constant worrying won't do you any good Mary, you can't change anything,' reproached Arthur, so Mary fell silent.

Within the week, Mary was troubled further, when it was announced that the government wanted everyone to have an identity card, not just for the purpose of collating information but they were thinking ahead, in case rationing had to be introduced. Every household was sent a registration form, to be completed on September 29th. Whilst just a formality for most people, it was more of a problem for Mary, as details of everyone's name, age and marital status were required.

Over the years, Mary had never been caught out, with either her new identity, the deception of lowering her age or her bigamous

148

marriage. Even Arthur still believed he'd married a spinster and, incredible as it seemed, thought that she was nine years younger than her actual age of fifty. Mary had convinced herself that she had got away with her lies, especially as nobody from Durham had ever contacted her or sought her out, but now, was there a chance, her deceit would come to light?

She chided herself for telling such a fib about her age in the first place and even considered whether it was time to come clean to her family, in order to avoid future problems. But then, she told herself, that might lead to some tricky questions and she was adamant that neither Tom nor Rosa should ever find out she wasn't legally married to their father. She could, though, do without all this stress. She had enough to deal with, worrying over the safety of her children, without concerns over their legitimacy. So, there was only one way forward, she must continue her lies when completing the form and just hope, no-one would ever be any the wiser.

Over the following weeks, Mary had a further difficult decision to make.

Manchester had now become a prime target for enemy attack, for, as Arthur was quick to point out, the city was an important inland port and it had many industries, some of which manufactured air craft and munitions.

'No wonder them Germans keep attacking, they want to destroy the supply lines and demolish all the factories at Trafford Park,' he explained.

The government, fully aware of the dangers in the big cities, were keen to safeguard all children and so they decided to set up 'Operation Pied Piper'.

'It's been proposed that all children, living within the city, are evacuated to rural areas,' Arthur informed his family one evening, realising that Rosa was eligible.

'I want you to be safe Rosa but I'm a bit reluctant to let you go,' Mary admitted to her daughter, who seemed quite unperturbed by the prospect.

'Most of the other children at school will be going, I'm sure,' Rosa assured her mother, 'so their mothers can't be too concerned.'

Mary stared hard at her daughter, realising how much she was growing up and what an attractive teenager she was becoming. She had pretty features, with her father's dark hair colouring and a vibrant, outgoing personality to match. This caused Mary some concerns. She didn't want her to be on the receiving end of any unwelcome attention, particularly as she was not yet fourteen. She remembered, only too well, how easily she had found herself in trouble, at a young age.

Mary was also aware that they seemed to have argued a lot recently, over silly things, such as Rosa wanting to wear lipstick, but the real issue was over her daughter's future plans. Rosa was showing real promise with her dancing ability and harboured a desire to pursue a career on the stage. Mary was adamant that it was not a respectable profession. She'd allowed her to take part in the local pantomimes at The Palace Theatre but when she was invited to join the dancing troupe at Blackpool Tower, Mary was horrified.

'You're not going on the stage. You can't go, you're a good girl!'

Rosa found her mother's double standards surprising, having been told by Mary so often, that she too loved dancing as a young girl and had once longed for a life under the bright lights of a stage.

In the end, Mary concluded, if she allowed Rosa to be evacuated, all thoughts of stardom might be put to one side. A period of separation would also have the added benefit of encouraging her to be independent plus she'd experience a completely different way of life, which must be to Rosa's advantage.

'I've been talking it over with your father and we've decided it might be best for you to be evacuated. You must promise though to write to us and keep us informed of your circumstances,' Mary informed her a few days later.

Rosa, feeling slightly irritated, reassured her, 'Don't be silly mother, you know I'll write to you.' And with that promise, her mother was appeased.

So, one morning, in early 1940, Rosa, accompanied by her mother, walked to school, wearing her gabardine mackintosh and her school hat and carrying a small bag of clothes and personal items. On their arrival, Rosa was given a square box, containing a gas mask and a label, to pin on her coat, which stated her name, address, school and destination. Then along with forty of her school friends, she was escorted by her teachers, onto a bus travelling to the railway station.

When the time came for mother and daughter to part, Mary felt such sadness and foreboding, that tears filled her eyes. Rosa, excited at first, saw her mother's reaction and struggled to stay composed.

Mary clung to her daughter until the last moment.

'Here's some food for the journey,' she said as she gave Rosa a bag containing a sandwich, an apple and some chocolate.

Rosa took it gratefully and gave her mother a final hug.

'Love you,' Mary called,' Don't forget to write!' but with all the children's excited chatter and the parent's cries, Mary doubted that Rosa had heard her.

After a long journey, through the countryside, the children arrived at a school where host families were waiting to take them to their new homes or 'billets' as they were called. The children assembled in a row, and one by one they were chosen. When she realised she was the last child to be picked, Rosa burst into tears, thinking her poor appearance was the cause of her rejection.

A very well to do lady spoke up, 'Oh well, I'll take her,' she said rather disdainfully, aware that if she refused the child, she would be fined. 'Come with me,' she ordered, as she took Rosa by the arm, 'I hope you've been brought up well and you know how to conduct yourself.'

Rosa wasn't sure exactly what the lady was inferring, so she smiled, gratefully. On seeing the lady's house for the first time, she was quite excited, having never experienced any place quite so grand or sumptuous. Being chosen last, has worked to my advantage, she thought to herself, maybe my friends haven't found for themselves such luxurious accommodation.

The reality turned out to be quite different for whilst the house may have been superior, Rosa was treated as totally inferior, in fact no better than a servant. Immediately, she was set to work, with an endless list of chores. When nighttime finally came, she longed for a warm, comfortable bed but was shocked when she was shown into a tiny, cold room in the attic, with a simple camp bed.

Over the following days, Rosa found life intolerable. She attempted to write a letter to her parents, begging to return home but unfortunately the lady discovered it. She immediately threatened to send her home on the next train, but then thought better of it, as she was claiming money for her, collecting it weekly from the Post Office. By way of punishment, she cruelly intercepted all of Rosa's future letters and destroyed them.

Back in Manchester, Mary was most concerned when she heard no news. She was upset that Rosa had broken her promise.

'I can't understand it,' she complained to Arthur, 'why isn't she letting us know how she's getting on?'

'Stop worrying Mary,' he told her, 'she's perhaps having such good fun that she hasn't found the time to sit down and write.'

Mary wasn't convinced and her anxiety increased with every passing day.

'That's it,' she informed Arthur, after yet another day with no news, 'we must go to visit her and soon.'

Arthur reluctantly agreed and they journeyed by train the next week. When they arrived and discovered just how badly Rosa had been treated, Mary was absolutely furious. Her anger boiled over,

'How dare you treat my Rosa like that,' she screamed and after pushing the lady onto the floor, she commanded Rosa.

'Get your coat, we're going home,'

'It was awful mother,' Rosa explained later, 'I spent nearly every day cleaning the house and scrubbing the floors.'

'I wonder how she liked having a taste of her own medicine,' Mary replied. 'Didn't I really wipe the floor with her!'

Mother and daughter both chuckled loudly but Arthur was more serious.

'I've been thinking Mary. It's not safe for Rosa to return to Manchester, why don't we send her to my Aunt Annie's house in Newtown?'

Mary was unsure and needed Rosa's assurance that she was happy to go to Wales.

'You'll like being at your Aunt Annie's, won't you Rosa? ' she questioned 'I know Aunt Annie will like having you, as she's no children of her own.'

Turning to Arthur, she added,

'We'll have to pay her of course but knowing your aunt, she won't charge us much.'

Rosa agreed, she'd enjoyed holidays in the past at her aunt's house and was willing to go for a while at least, so the necessary arrangements were made.

Aunt Annie was indeed delighted to have Rosa and treated her like a daughter, teaching her many new skills, including how to milk a cow, how to whitewash a tree to discourage insects and how to knit socks using four needles.

Mary missed her terribly but she was grateful that Rosa was safe, especially now the ensuing war was entering a new stage. Manchester became the target of heavy bombardment, by the Luftwaffe, the Nazi German Air Force. Almost night after night, a siren blared out, warning of air raids and Mary, Arthur and Tom took to hiding in the under stairs' cupboard, waiting until the 'All Clear' signal came.

Mary pondered how different it was to the Great War. Then she had been largely unaware of the awful atrocities of trench warfare but now she could see first- hand the devastating effects of the bombs and hear the awful noise of the explosions. Bright lights constantly flooded the sky, followed by destructive fires, which filled the air with acrid smoke. The heaviest assault was usually over the city centre, focusing on factories, but the explosions were indiscriminate. This wasn't just men fighting men, Mary deliberated, it had gone beyond that and now women and children were being killed, which she found quite unbearable. But then she thought back to the sinking of the liner, 'The Lusitania' in 1915. Hadn't the Germans indiscriminately killed women and children back then?

Then within months, Rosa wrote to say she was homesick and wanted to return to Manchester but Mary was perturbed,

'It's not really safe, is it, Arthur? I think we should insist that she stay in Wales.'

'Don't be concerned Mary, she's growing up now, it's time she made her own decisions,' Arthur said, trying to pacify his wife.

But Mary was anxious and she became edgy and withdrawn.

Her fears were compounded when Rosa arrived home just before Christmas 1940, which proved to be badly timed. The Christmas Blitz was about to hit Manchester and it was to last for the next eight months. The family talked of nothing else.

Tom, in his youthful innocence, was concerned over the Manchester United ground.

'I hear Old Trafford has taken a hit and the bombs have wrecked the pitch and demolished some of the stadium.'

'At least no one was killed, Tom, just think of all those families whose lives have been destroyed by the bombs,' his mother reminded him.

Arthur was fearful for Prestwich Hospital, 'I've been told Salford Royal Hospital has been badly damaged and fourteen nurses have been killed,' he announced one evening in June, 'I hope it's not us next.'

This caused Mary to panic even more, yet there was no escape. Her misery continued.

'Now I'm eighteen, I have to enrol, so I'm going to join the navy,' Tom announced in the autumn of 1941.

'That's a good choice, Tom, we're so proud of you,' his father replied.

Mary was in turmoil but she forced herself to stay silent. She didn't want him to go, for the possibility of losing her son in warfare was unbearable. Yet what choice did he have?

A few days later, Tom had packed ready for departure.

'Promise me you'll come back,' Mary begged as he prepared to leave, 'Remember that you and Rosa are all I've got, apart from your dad of course.'

'Mother, I'm grown up now, I'll be back safe, I promise,' Tom whispered as he gave her a final embrace.

Mary worked hard to hold back the tears but as soon as he left, she was inconsolable and took several days to settle. The house seemed so quiet and Mary missed him dreadfully, not just his company but there was less need to cook and clean. Arthur suggested, with an empty room, they could make their own contribution to the war effort, by advertising for a lodger. This, he hoped, might take her mind off things and give a boost to their income.

'You get the highest marks in the area for having the best place to board,' Gerry Trainor told Mary several weeks later. Gerry had come to Manchester to work in the local ICI factory and had responded to Mary's advert, placed in the corner shop, advertising a room to rent.

He appreciated Mary's efforts to give him the comforts of home.

'You treat me like one of the family, you're always putting yourself out to make sure I'm well fed and happy,' he remarked, as once again Mary had produced a tasty meal, despite the restraints of rationing.

Mary was genuinely pleased with his comments. She liked Gerry; he was a typical Irishman, always full of charm and wit and his humour often lightened her mood. She was happy to work hard, as it helped the days to pass and meant less time was spent worrying over Tom.

The year passed by and the war continued with little sign of any resolution. In the latter months of 1942, seventeen-year-old Rosa decided that she too would like to join the war effort. She wanted to enlist in the Women's Royal Navy Service known as the WRENS, which provided a supporting role, carrying out all kinds of back up duties.

At first, Mary was horrified and refused point blank to allow it. Even Arthur was reluctant to agree. However, Rosa assured them that she wouldn't be placed in situations of high risk so after much persuasion and coercion, her father relented and eventually managed to persuade Mary to give her permission.

Rosa journeyed down to London by train and spent her first nights in a city that was facing even greater bombardment than Manchester. She listened in terror as the aircraft dropped their bombs, never knowing exactly where they would land. Rosa found it very frightening and quickly appreciated why her mother had been so concerned over her safety.

Just three months into her training, Rosa received some bad news. Her brother's convoy ship had been torpedoed three times, whilst on the Icelandic Murmansk run. The ship was taking supplies to the Soviet port but all the men knew it was a dangerous mission, with a constant threat of attack. Tom ended up, stranded in the freezing water, before being rescued. He had been taken, in a serious condition, to The Royal Naval Military Hospital in Chatham, Kent. Rosa rushed to visit him...

Back in Manchester, Mary was mortified - this was the worst news possible.

'Arthur, I knew something like this would happen,' she raged bitterly.

The following weeks cast a shadow over her life. Unable to visit Tom, she was constantly fretful and stressed, taking her feelings out on her husband.

'You were the one who encouraged him to join the navy,' she chided, 'it's your fault that he's now lying injured.'

'Mary, that's really not fair,' he told her, 'you're being very unreasonable. Tom was old enough to make his own choices, we couldn't have stopped him.'

Arthur of course, had no awareness of her pain at losing her first husband in World War One, so equally had no understanding of her paranoia that something bad would undoubtedly happen to one of her present family. He tried to be patient with her but found her low mood very hard to deal with. He was determined to stay positive but Mary found it increasingly difficult, having to hold such a dark secret in her heart.

She was greatly relieved as Tom made a slow but full recovery, after spending many weeks in hospital. She was also delighted when, after six months, Rosa moved away from the dangers of life in London, enrolling instead as a switch board operator, on a training ship on the River Mersey, at Warrington, Lancashire.

It wasn't long before Rosa informed her parents that, as well as being content in her work, she'd also met the man who she was sure would be her future husband.

'There Mary, what did I tell you,' Arthur reminded her, 'you waste so much energy with all your worrying when there's really no need for it.'

Mary had to admit he was right - she was heartened by how happy Rosa seemed to be and for her assurances that she was safe, especially now that she seemed to have a caring young man to look after her. She was even more relieved when, in May 1945, it was announced that the war had ended successfully. The Allies had accepted Germany's surrender, a week after Adolf Hitler had committed suicide.

Arthur and Mary celebrated, 'Victory in Europe' day on

May 8th, joining with their neighbours and friends. There was much singing, dancing and excitement as everyone gathered along their packed street. Finally the bleak days of war were over and there was a general feeling of optimism, everyone hopeful that better days were ahead. Mary began to feel more relaxed and gradually her spirit of fun returned but she hardly dare believe that her happiness would last.

TWENTY-SIX
Durham/Bath – 1939-1946

Throughout the war years, Mary had been totally unaware that three of her other children were fighting in the forces. She had chosen to put them to the back of her mind and appeared to be successful in her quest to deny their existence, although there were times, especially on significant dates, when uncomfortable memories would flood back.

Each one of them had struggled to come to terms with the aftermath of being abandoned and for some, it still overshadowed their lives.

Her eldest child Jacob, enrolled in the Durham Light Infantry in 1939, fulfilling his childhood vow, to follow in his father's footsteps and by 1943 he was in the Military Police.

Life had been very difficult for him over recent years, still scarred by his mother's rejection. In 1923, aged fifteen, he'd run away from his foster home and eventually travelled down south and joined the Royal Artillery at Topsham Barracks in Exeter. Whilst there, he'd met a young widow and then, discovering she was expecting his child, he married her in 1931. Five children had followed but Jacob had been a poor father and husband, going absent without leave on many occasions and deserting his family. Now he'd left them permanently and they had no notion that he'd gone back up north and joined a different regiment. They had only sad and resentful feelings towards their father.

Meanwhile, his younger brother Roland - who now called himself Ron - had joined the navy and been able to carve a successful career for himself, determined never to let his difficult childhood mar his life. In 1928, at fifteen, he'd responded to a naval recruitment poster and had slowly risen up the ranks. By 1944, he was a Chief Petty Officer, taking command in the D-Day landings, in which soldiers were transported onto the Normandy beaches, to begin a major offensive against the Germans.

He'd always felt it his duty to maintain the unity of the family, despite their early trauma and he made it his responsibility to keep in contact with his sister Ann and his younger brother, John-George, now known as John, although all contact with his elder brother Jacob had been lost.

John hadn't enlisted in the forces in 1939, as his job as a

157

fitter at Stothers and Pitts engineering firm, in Bath, was deemed important war work. The renowned factory had received a visit from Queen Mary in recognition of their vital contribution to the war and John was delighted when his hand was shaken by royalty. He was later to have a wartime wedding, in 1944, to a girl named Mary, whom he met on one of his visits to his sister Ann.

Their sister Ann had fulfilled her childhood pact with her friend, Edith Lough and moved away from Durham when she was eighteen in 1928 and gone to a seaside town, as they'd agreed. Edith had found work in Scarborough and sent word to Ann that there was a job available as a lady's maid, if Ann would like it. Ann didn't hesitate and soon found herself working as a domestic servant for a Mrs Mabel Gardiner-Smith. Next door, to the house where she worked, was a guesthouse, run by two sisters, whom Ann befriended. They introduced her to their brother Herbert, who was a farmer from Burton Pidsea, a small village in the East Riding of Yorkshire. In 1937, Ann married Herbert and they moved into a detached bungalow on the outskirts of the village. During the early forties, both Ann and Herbert became air raid wardens, as their contribution to the war effort.

Occasionally Ron would visit, whilst on leave, bringing gifts of tinned meat, sugar, tea, cheese and fruit. Ann was delighted with these 'luxuries' and in turn Ron appreciated the peace of village life, after his fraught convoy missions.

Neither Ann, nor her siblings, had any idea that they had a half-brother, Oswald, who was now residing in Winterton Lunatic Asylum near Sedgefield, County Durham. After being classed 'mentally defective' as a child, the label had stuck and he'd been living in the asylum for all his adult life. Winterton was a town in its own right, with, amongst other things, its own shops, gym, dentist, football pitch and even its own fire station. Under staff supervision, Oswald cultivated the land and tended the animals in which he found some solace but he had always suffered ill health and was a sad, lonely individual.

In 1946, when twenty-eight, he caught pneumonia and died. On completing their log book, the Registrar at the asylum, recorded Oswald's death with a single straight black line crossed through the space marked, 'Name of relative to whom death notice sent.' Oswald's passing was a totally insignificant event to those beyond the asylum. To his siblings, he was non-existent and as for his mother, Mary, there was absolutely no awareness of the tragedy of his short, sad life.

Also residing in Durham, was Mary's sixth child Ivan and he too was unknown by any of his half brothers and sisters. As he was growing up, he rarely thought of his mother as he neither knew her nor had any feelings towards her. To him she was a total stranger and as such he was totally indifferent. Just once he asked his father Allan what had happened to his mother and he simply replied, 'Your mother liked dancing and the bright lights of the city, so she simply deserted us.'

Ivan accepted this explanation and spent his adult life with no more thought of his mother. He became a miner, married a local girl Jean and in 1939, he joined the army and was posted to Burma where he spent two years. Ivan proved himself very capable and rose through the ranks from Lance Corporal to Staff Sergeant. His father Allan never remarried and died alone in 1941, his true age finally revealed on his death certificate as seventy-three.

In Manchester, life for Mary and Arthur slowly returned to normality, although the problems associated with rationing lasted until 1954. Arthur continued his daily shift at the hospital whilst Mary supplemented his wages with cleaning jobs, working for the wealthier immigrant families who'd moved into the area, after the war. Various lodgers came and went but life seemed rather dull, especially with Rosa and Tom no longer around.

'How would you feel if Jack and I married and we came to live with you?' Rosa asked her mother one day in the summer of 1947.

'You're not in the family way are you?' Mary asked rather bluntly.

'Certainly not!' Rosa replied, 'it's just that we want to get married in September but we can't afford a home of our own at the moment... though we are saving up.'

Mary didn't need to consider the request, once reassured that her daughter had not done anything she considered 'shameful'.

'Of course you can come here to live,' she replied, 'and we best start saving our clothing coupons for your wedding dress.'

'I'm planning to have it made,' Rosa explained, 'but I'll maybe have to borrow some dresses for the bridesmaids.'

'When your dad and I married, we didn't even have bridesmaids,' Mary told her, but omitted the fact that she was expecting a baby at the time!

It was just a year after the marriage, that Rosa gave birth to a little girl whom she called Caroline. Mary enjoyed looking after the baby whilst Rosa continued to work and soon formed a strong, close bond with her grandchild.

Occasionally, as she sat cradling the infant, old memories surfaced and Mary's mind drifted back to the past, especially to

Ann, her first daughter. How different her life would have been if John-George had returned from the war unscathed, she would surely never have abandoned her children. But then conversely she reasoned if she hadn't come to Manchester, she would never have met Arthur and certainly wouldn't be sat now, holding this beautiful granddaughter.

TWENTY-SEVEN
Manchester – 1951

One evening in the Spring of 1951, Rosa walked in from work to find Mary in floods of tears.

'Whatever's the matter ma - is Caroline alright?' Rosa asked anxiously, assuming her daughter must be the cause of Mary's distress.

Mary shook her head in response, 'Caroline's fine,' she whispered.

Rosa pressed her, 'So what is it ma?'

Despite her persistence, Mary refused to say. Glum faced and with her usual ruddy complexion now ashen, she sat and stared into the distance, constantly dabbing her red rimmed eyes with her handkerchief.

When Arthur returned home later, Mary's tears returned but even he couldn't persuade his wife to disclose what was troubling her.

'Is it something you've done or has somebody done something to you?' he asked trying to prompt her into a reply. But she just wasn't forthcoming.

Finally even Arthur, known for his placid nature, became exasperated and insisted she tell him what was the cause of her misery:

'How can anyone help you, if we've no idea what the problem is,' he pleaded, 'besides nothing's so bad that it can't be sorted out.' Arthur was almost shouting now.

'But that's where you're wrong Arthur, this can never be put right.'

Having managed to finally coax her into speaking, Arthur encouraged her further...

'What do you mean – this can never be put right? What are you referring to? Just sit down and share with me what's happened.'

He gently took hold of Mary's hands, which were shaking and stared at her lovingly. The room went quiet as hesitantly, Mary tried to explain:

'Two men called at the house this morning. I was not sure at first exactly who they were but they looked very official. They were wearing dark suits with waistcoats and they had them bowler hats on. When I asked who they were, they produced their identity cards and explained they were government officials.'

'But what were they wanting?' interrupted Arthur rather impatiently, keen that she move on with the story and disclose the cause of her misery.

'Well I didn't understand at first. They were showing me some forms with my personal details on and they kept saying the information that was written down was misleading and could I clarify it. But I didn't know what they were referring to.'

'I think I might know,' Arthur butted in again. 'Was it to do with the government census?'

Arthur recalled that he had filled in a detailed questionnaire, just a few weeks previously, one Sunday evening in April. It had been twenty years since the previous census and so this one had been particularly rigorous. He'd had to state as head of the household, how long they'd been married, where and when they'd both been born and how many children they had had, even if they were no longer alive. Then, it suddenly struck Arthur why maybe Mary was so distressed.

'They didn't go on to mention William, did they, is that why you're so upset Mary?'

'No, no it wasn't about our children. They said they hadn't got the correct details about me.'

'How do you mean?' Arthur asked, puzzled by her remark.

'Well they asked me for my place and date of birth... then they wanted to know my mother and father's names... where I was born... to whom was I married... in fact endless questions, some of which I struggled to answer. It all became too much for me... I was so flustered... but then at the end, after double checking my details on the form he was holding, the second man, who'd been silent up to that point, uttered some words I'll never forget.'

At this point, Mary lowered her head and Arthur had to cajole her to continue.

'He told me, in no uncertain terms, that according to their records, under my given maiden name of Margaret Mary Purvis and my stated place of birth as Spennymoor, County Durham, there is no such person. According to them, I DON'T EXIST!'

'What do you mean, you don't exist!' Arthur repeated the phrase trying to understand it himself.

'I don't know Arthur, I don't know. I don't understand why they're saying that they've no record of me. All I do know is that it frightened me very much.'

'Then what did they do? How did they leave it?' Arthur was becoming irritated now, not so much with Mary, more with the

162

men, whoever they were they had no right to upset his wife like this.

'As the two men turned to go, they gave me a final threat, saying they'll be coming back when they've got it sorted.'

'There, there, Mary, don't you worry,' Arthur said reassuringly as he patted her arm, 'You've nothing to hide so there's no need to concern yourself, is there?'

Mary looked directly at him. For a moment she was tempted to blurt out the truth but then thought better of it. She shook her head, looked down again and said nothing.

But over the following days, she continued to fret - nothing any of her family said or did gave her any comfort. The family were fully aware that she could be inclined to dark moods but usually she would bounce back from any adversity. This time seemed different, she seemed truly heartbroken.

The words, 'We'll be back,' resounded in Mary's ears and the fear that was raging in her mind was tangible. How could she tell her family the true reasons for her panic? Was her secret past about to be revealed and all her lies about to be uncovered?

What if the authorities found out she was a bigamist?

Could she be imprisoned?

Indeed one of the reasons she'd never gone back to Durham was a fear of being caught and possibly jailed. Yet this was not just a dread of prosecution, it was much more to do with the fact that if her bigamy came to light, her children might be declared illegitimate. The shame of that would be too much and the effect of it too great.

Would Arthur stop loving her? Was there a remote possibility that she might lose this family as well?

Mary was tormented and racked with guilt, she dearly wanted to be truthful and reveal her past but stopped short, knowing it would surely hurt them too much. She acknowledged that her many untruths had produced such a web of deceit that she was trapped. It was not a good feeling. But if the truth was disclosed, it could cause even worse heartache.

She decided instead, to plead ignorance: 'What does it all mean, Arthur? Why are they saying I don't exist!' she repeated on a daily basis, sobbing as she did so.

'Don't worry mother,' was all Thomas could think to say when he called round and was upset to find his mother crying. He didn't know how best to comfort her. Rosa simply gave her mother reassuring hugs and as for Arthur, he tried to make light of it, in his typical positive manner.

For the next few days and weeks, Maggie was on edge, especially whenever there was a knock at the door. But that knock, the one she dreaded the most, never came:

'They must have realised that they'd made a clerical error,' Arthur concluded some time later.

And Mary was more than happy to agree...

TWENTY-EIGHT
Manchester – 1951 onwards

That incident really unsettled Mary. She began to dwell on the reality of what she had actually done. Up until now, she had tried to block out the past, to such an extent that it was a real shock when she was forced to confront the truth. Really she was living a lie but she was desperate not to be found out. She would never want to lose her husband's love for she recognised that he had brought stability to her life and she didn't want her children to think badly of her.

She recalled the lies she had told Arthur, her third husband, almost thirty years earlier. She'd said she was twenty-five on her wedding day in 1923, when really she had been almost thirty-four. She'd told him that her name was Margaret Mary Purvis but insisted she wanted to be called Mary. She'd told him she was a spinster when really she had been married twice before and was still married to her second husband, Allan Fenwick. She'd said her father was John Purvis when in fact he was called Jacob Burns. If she'd told him the truth back then, would he ever have wanted to marry her? Not that legally she was free to do so anyway. Should she ever tell him the full extent of her lies or would it shock him too much? He had believed her when she said she was single and this, she felt, was her most damning lie. If she revealed her deceit, all trust might be lost. Besides if the truth came out it would mean that this marriage was...

No she couldn't possibly tell him! Certainly she didn't want her two children to know her secrets. Discovering they had five half-brothers and a half-sister who they had never met, would be difficult, impossible even, for them to accept. Maybe though, it would ease her mind if she revealed just some of her deceit - her real age at least, that wouldn't hurt, especially if she made a joke of it. But the rest better be her secret and her secret only. She would though, she decided, retain the one thing that betrayed her past life. She would keep it safe and not show anybody. One day surely it might be found but only when it wouldn't matter - years ahead, when she was dead and gone. Yes, that's what she would do. She was happy now she'd made up her mind.

One evening, when Arthur was smoking his pipe, sat in his

favourite armchair by the fire, she sneaked up to their bedroom. She scrambled around in her old battered suitcase, the very one she had brought with her from Durham to Manchester. Yes there it was - the one piece of paper that identified her - it was not lost. She looked at it one last time.

It was the proof of her past and now it would be left for the future. She found an old biscuit tin in the bottom of her double, free standing wardrobe, the one that also contained a few old photographs and she popped it in, right underneath, at the bottom, where no one would see it. Next, she carefully placed the tin inside the suitcase, locked it and hauled it on top of the wardrobe so it was hidden from view. But what to do with the key? I know just the right place, she thought, as she opened the drawer at the bottom of the wardrobe and spotted her handbag...

Mary felt a sense of ease. She was happy knowing that her secret was now hidden more securely and only the most determined person would uncover it. She had, she felt, kept her present family from finding out about her torrid past which would have only brought them sadness and shame. She would, she told herself, continue to enjoy her family and let go of the guilt.

All she needed now was an opportunity to reveal her true age to Arthur. Mary decided that it must be soon, for if she left it too long she might not do it at all. So, a few days later, she cooked Arthur his favourite meal of steak and onion pie followed by suet pudding and then suggested, 'It's such a lovely summer evening, why don't we go for a stroll in Heaton Park after we've eaten our meal?'

Arthur was happy to agree as he and Mary had enjoyed many happy hours there and they both liked nothing better than a relaxing walk, seeing it as free entertainment as well as a chance to breathe some fresh air. For Arthur, it was a welcome break away from the steamy atmosphere of the laundry and Mary simply enjoyed being out in the open.

On their arrival, Mary took Arthur's arm and together they laughed and giggled as they enjoyed watching the antics of the ducks and then sat down to rest on a wooden bench.

'Arthur, there's something I want to ask you,' Mary began nervously, 'but I'm a bit worried what you'll say.'

'What is it?' Arthur asked, concerned, as her tone of voice indicated it might be something serious.

'You wouldn't ever leave me, would you Arthur?'

Quite taken aback by her words, he responded immediately.

'Never, ever, ever,' he repeated emphatically.

'Even if you find out I've done something wicked,' she said

as tears welled up in her eyes.

Arthur was now quite anxious, wondering just what his wife had done to prompt this discussion. Wicked? What could she have done to justify calling herself wicked? His thoughts even turned to adultery, had his wife been unfaithful? Surely not, he couldn't bear to even think of it.

'Better blurt it out Mary, what have you done?' he responded.

'I don't know why Arthur, I can't explain it but Arthur when I met you,' and then she paused, fearing to say the words, 'When I met you I... I lied about my age.'

Arthur breathed a sigh of relief. Compared to what he was expecting, lying about her true age seemed a minor misdemeanour.

'Is that it?' he asked. Have you been worrying yourself over that? You better tell me your true age, I guess you're a bit older than you've led me to believe all these years.'

'Yes Arthur, I am,' Mary said blushing, 'I'm not fifty-four like you thought I was, I'm actually sixty-one.'

'Sixty-one!' he repeated, as he sought to take it in, 'talk about pulling the wool over your husband's eyes.'

Arthur was quiet for a while and Mary feared for what he was thinking.

'Well Mary,' he said staring at her intensely, 'you don't half look good for your age!'

'Thank you, thank you, for being so understanding and even able to joke about it,' Mary replied, giving him an embrace. Despite her obvious relief, her tears continued, but not out of sadness. It was such a weight off her mind, knowing this aspect of her deceit was finally out in the open.

'I'm going to be serious now though, Mary, I still love you and I always will but please reassure me that it's your only lie and that you're not hiding something. You've always been faithful to me, haven't you?'

Mary was glad she could answer him truthfully, on the issue of her fidelity at least.

'Of course, I've always been faithful to you. Since the day I met you, there has never been anyone else for me. I love you deeply and I always will.'

Arthur happily accepted her answer, having no idea that she was still withholding other secrets. He paused before adding, 'I've just had a thought, Mary, I think we've solved a mystery at last,'

'What do you mean, Arthur?' she asked.

'It's just come to me,' he continued, ' I'm thinking this false date of birth could be the very reason why the census men said you didn't exist. They wouldn't be able to find you in their records, if we gave them a false age and birth date.'

Mary agreed, 'That's a possibility Arthur,' she said, before deciding to leave it at that. She had vowed never to tell anyone her other lies, not even Arthur and so that had to be the end of her revelations. But she was pleased that Arthur now knew, and accepted, her real age and it was, she acknowledged, a good feeling. She stood up from the bench.

'I think it's time to go home Arthur, it's been a long day.'

'You're right Mary,' he agreed, but I'm going home a happier man. It's good to know you'll be getting your old age pension much sooner than I thought you would!' and they both roared with laughter.

TWENTY-NINE
Ten years later, Manchester – 1960s

By the early sixties, Mary's health began to deteriorate, she was becoming more confused on a daily basis. Her balance, increasingly unsteady, caused her to have regular falls and she became daunted by familiar tasks. Arthur was very supportive despite struggling himself with failing health. He was stressed to watch as his wife of nearly forty years began to suffer. He saw it as his duty to do whatever was needed to keep her out of hospital. As a result, household chores were often disregarded and meal times became a constant problem for an ill-trained, undomesticated man like Arthur. It fell to Rosa and her husband, plus Tom and his wife, to call round on a regular basis, to check on them both.

By early January 1962, Mary became seriously ill and took to her bed. She died a few days later. The family paid tribute to her in the local press - the Manchester Evening News. The entry in the deaths' column read:

CANNON: On January 14th at 35 Egmont Street, after much suffering patiently born, Margaret Mary aged 72 years, dearly loved wife of Arthur Herbert Cannon and dear mother of Thomas and Rosa. Service and committal at Blackley Crematorium.

Arthur was distraught and lost his zest for life. He felt unable to stay in the home that they had created together. Rosa and her husband suggested that he went to live with them, in a newly acquired house in Parkhurst Road, Manchester, an offer that he willingly agreed to.

Rosa, struggling with her grief, left it a while before she could face going back to clear out her parent's home and possessions. It was too hard to accept her mother had gone and wouldn't be coming back.

With pressure growing, as the house needed re-letting, Rosa accepted she would have to make a start. Early one morning, she took the bus to her childhood home, determined to work hard and see the job completed. As she stepped into the house from off the pavement, she soon realised that this wasn't going to be either easy or quick.

There was nothing of monetary value but Mary had enjoyed creating a cosy, tidy home filled with basic but functional pieces of furniture. There was a large mahogany china cabinet in the living room that needed emptying, which was full of a wide assortment of cheap pottery and glassware. A rectangular table, covered in an oilcloth, and with a large oil lamp standing on top of it, was placed by the opposite wall. Nearby was Mary's rocking chair, where she had spent many happy hours in front of the coal fire, sitting next to Arthur. Rosa went to sit in it for just a few minutes whilst she came to terms with what she was about to do. She didn't want to dispose of anything but realistically she knew there wasn't enough room in her own house to enable her to keep much.

She decided to begin upstairs and work her way downwards. It was quite basic in each of the three bedrooms, with only a bed, a small dresser with a wash basin and jug and a wardrobe, all standing on linoleum flooring. In the main bedroom was a double free standing wardrobe and that's what Rosa decided she would clear first.

She began by working through the long row of garments that were hung in the main body of the robe. Rosa knew her mother had never been extravagant with clothes - but equally she had never thrown items away. Both her upbringing and the war years had made her thrifty and unwilling to part with anything. Rosa spotted her mother's favourite polyester floral dress with its flowing skirt - the material had been such a new innovation in the fifties and as such had become her mother's pride and joy. Rosa touched it lovingly and thought of how much both she and her mother had always loved dancing. On the top shelf of the wardrobe was Mary's large collection of hats.

Arthur could never understand why Mary would want to hide her beautiful auburn rich hair, under any form of headgear but all ladies felt undressed if they didn't have a hat for every occasion and Mary was no exception. Rosa picked up individual ones and thought back to when her mother had worn them. Her favourites she remembered, were her straw hat - which she always referred to as her 'bengie' and wore every summer - and her navy cloche hat, which she had worn on her very first outing with Arthur.

There was also a large drawer below the cavernous body of the robe. Rosa struggled to pull it open as it had warped over time especially due to the dampness caused by the unheated room. Its contents were not exciting: a few ex-army blankets, a couple of pairs of shoes and an odd, cheap handbag or two.

She smiled as she picked out the comb from deep within one of the bags - for there were still a few auburn hairs clinging to its teeth. There was also an old key and a well used buttonhook inside. Rosa could almost visualise herself as a child watching her mother use the hook on her boots, which she always wore in the winter.

Two inner pockets, inside the hand bag's black lining, revealed an almost white cotton handkerchief, with pretty embroidery, in one and a powder compact in the other. She felt, because these objects were her mother's personal possessions, she shouldn't be even considering throwing them away. Rosa knew there was nothing of any worth but so many of the objects evoked happy memories and it was hard to dispose of them. Also in the drawer was a well-worn tin containing a few of her father's old clay pipes. The smell of them instantly reminded her of the evenings when he'd sat by the open fire, enjoying his smoke. It brought back even earlier memories when as a child, her father had lifted her on his lap, pipe in one hand and his free arm round her shoulder, telling her stories from his own childhood back in London.

Yet amongst all Mary's possessions, Rosa found nothing from her mother's early life - no photographs, no letters or any childhood mementoes. It struck Rosa that she knew very little of her mother's family background. Only rarely had she talked about her time in Spennymoor, where she'd told them she was born. They'd often teased her about her Durham accent and the strange way she pronounced words such as 'booook' and 'cooook'.

Rosa recalled her mother telling her once that her father had been killed in a mining accident but she didn't even know his name. Neither had her mother ever spoken of her real mother. She had mentioned that she had a stepmother who she hadn't particularly liked but who'd involved her with her role as midwife to the villagers. Rosa paused, considering why they, as a family, had never been to visit Spennymoor, probably the cost would have been too great, she concluded. Money had always been so tight.

I just wish I'd asked my mother more, she mused, although she never seemed to want to talk of her past life, especially after the incident with the census men in 1951. That, she recalled, had been such a strange episode and her mother's reaction to it was etched in her memory. Why had she been so deeply affected by it and just what did they mean when they'd told her she didn't exist?

It was all somewhat of a mystery but Rosa guessed there was no way to ever solve it... Rosa stopped daydreaming and returned to the task in hand. After completely emptying the entire wardrobe, she set out to give it a spring clean. It was long overdue. A fine dust clung to every surface and there was a musky smell within. Mother would be appalled, Rosa chided herself, she was so meticulous about keeping everything pristine.

She went to fetch the small wooden steps which were kept outside in the coal shed, within the back yard, hoping they would enable her to reach the very top of the wardrobe. Being quite small in stature, Rosa still struggled to gain enough height, despite perching on the highest step. As she swept across the surface, leaning over precariously, her hand knocked against what she thought was a box. She stretched out and tried to pick it up. It wasn't heavy but it was not going to be easy to lift it down. Fortunately she soon realised it had something like a handle which enabled her to gently lower it and reveal its identity. It was an old battered suitcase with metal clasps and a keyhole. Rosa couldn't ever recall seeing this before and questioned how long it had lain there.

She carefully climbed off the steps and lowered the case onto the linoleum flooring. She knelt against it and was desperately hoping it wouldn't be locked. But it was. How annoying. But then she had a thought - maybe just maybe that key would fit… now where had she seen it? Was it in the black handbag? Yes there it was at the bottom. Now would it fit, she wondered?

She was delighted to discover that it did. The case opened but when Rosa peered inside, its contents were rather disappointing. Just a simple biscuit tin, with a fading picture of a blue budgerigar, was lying underneath a few old blankets. Rosa smiled as she noticed the label was still attached 'Family Favourites' - yes Rosa remembered her mother was always partial to a biscuit - and the name was quite appropriate really for she had loved and favoured her family.

The tin was reluctant to open and reveal what was inside, as it had rusted over the years. But as Rosa clawed at the lid, it suddenly popped open, spilling its contents onto her lap. What was this? An old photograph of a soldier. He's rather handsome, Rosa thought to herself. The man looking back at her, must, she guessed, be in his late teens or early twenties. He looked rather dashing in his uniform and she presumed it must be her dad, though she barely recognised him. How disappointing that there was no name on the back. There were a few other pictures including a lovely one of Elizabeth, the family dog. Rosa recalled just how much she had loved her and remembered crying for a long time, when she'd died of old age. Amongst the photos, Rosa came across a slip of folded paper, all crumpled up and no longer its original crisp white, more yellowish with age. She opened it carefully, having no inkling of what it was about to reveal. The first thing she spotted was that it was a birth certificate Scanning it with great interest, she read the words that had been hand written so neatly in black ink. She was totally puzzled,

Parish: **Hensingham, Cumberland**
Date of birth: **June 16th 1889**

'Hensingham – I've never heard of it'…Rosa spoke out loud, as if she had an audience to acknowledge her confusion. Then she saw the name: ***Margaret Burns.***

'Who on earth is Margaret Burns?'

Rosa wrinkled her face as she tried to think. For a moment Rosa became lost in her own thoughts. The suitcase must surely have belonged to her mother - especially as it had the treasured photograph of Arthur inside. Could this certificate have some connection to her? The surname 'Burns' meant nothing to Rosa, but why would this certificate be amongst all her personal possessions if it had no relevance at all to Mary?

At that moment Rosa made a vow to herself. Sometime, in the future, she would investigate her mother's former life… she would try to find out if there was any link between Mary Cannon and Margaret Burns… she might even be able to solve the mystery of why her mother had been told she didn't exist. But, for now, she must get back to the job in hand…

THIRTY
Manchester – Spring 2004

Rosa was now seventy-seven and still residing, with her husband Jack, in Parkhill Avenue to the north west of the city. They lived alone. Arthur, her father, had died in 1972 and her daughter Caroline had left home at a similar time. Now happily married herself, she had blessed Rosa and Jack with two grandchildren whom they greatly cherished. Still active and in good health, Rosa enjoyed many social activities and was particularly looking forward to celebrating two major events on the horizon: her eightieth birthday in 2006 and their diamond wedding in 2007.

Yet thoughts of her past were not far from Rosa's mind. She had never forgotten strange incidents in her mother's life; men telling her she didn't exist and a mysterious birth certificate belonging to a Margaret Burns. Rosa had never made those enquiries, she'd promised herself back in the sixties but put this down to the fact she had been so busy, besides she had no idea where to begin.

After watching television with her husband one evening, her interest was reawakened.

'Do you know Jack, I'm wondering if my family has a great story waiting to be uncovered, just like that celebrity on 'Who do you think you are?'

'What makes you think that?' he asked, smiling at his wife's temerity.

'Can you remember, way back, after mother died, I found a mystery birth certificate amongst her possessions. I'd love to find out more 'cos I'm sure there's an interesting story there somewhere. '

'Why don't you have a word with our friend Roy, he's a bit of a family history buff, maybe he could help you?' Jack suggested.

'That's a really good idea, but first I better go and search out that certificate,' she said laughing, 'after all, it is over forty years ago since I last saw it!'

Several days later, with the certificate located, Rosa approached Roy and was delighted when he agreed to undertake some research.

'I think you might have some problems tracing my mother because I've been told she didn't exist!' Rosa joshed.

174

'Leave it with me, I'll do what I can,' Roy promised, quite intrigued, 'but be prepared – you never know what skeletons I might uncover!'

'As long as they're rich ones, I won't complain,' she retorted.

One hundred miles away, in Kingston upon Hull, a remarkably similar scenario was being played out in the Richardson household. Clive and Kath, both primary school teachers with two grown up children, Joanne and Simon, were also trying to solve a family mystery. For almost five years, they'd been researching Clive's mother's family history and had started to uncover an incredible story. Yet despite painstaking efforts, involving hundreds of hours of research, with additional help from Gareth Watkins, a genealogist at Hull Central Library, they still hadn't discovered what had happened to the central character in the story.

What was her name?

Margaret Burns, born in Whitehaven in 1889, who was in fact Clive's grandmother!

Clive had been brought up in the small village of Burton Pidsea, some ten miles east of the city. His mother Ann had rarely spoken of her childhood yet had intimated a deep sadness, saying that she was orphaned at an early age, her father had been killed in World War One and her mother had died soon after of the Spanish flu. This, Clive and Kath had discovered was not entirely true!

'I still find it hard to believe your grandmother didn't die of the flu but actually abandoned your mother plus her three brothers and then went on to have two more children and deserted them as well. She must have been very desperate at the time, as why else would she contemplate doing that?' Kath remarked after their latest investigations uncovered further startling revelations about Margaret.

Clive agreed, for he too was struggling to comprehend so many of his grandmother's actions. Annoyingly, though, despite endless inquiries, they still hadn't managed to discover what had happened to Margaret, after 1921, when she'd walked out on her second husband Allan and left her sixth child Ivan with a shopkeeper. She just seemed to have disappeared without trace!

'I think maybe, we'll have to accept that this is a mystery that will have to remain forever that,' Clive concluded. 'The final whereabouts of my grandmother is certainly an enigma but having deserted all her family, it's understandable that she wouldn't want to be traced.'

Manchester, 2005

In Manchester, several months passed before Roy contacted Rosa again, full of apologies, not only for the delay but because he'd made little headway. The only thing he could tell Rosa was that Margaret Burns had had an elder sister called Nancy, whose grandson was now residing in St Agnes, Cornwall.

'I contacted the grandson but unfortunately he couldn't tell me anything about Margaret and he certainly didn't know of any Burns' family connection to Manchester,' Roy explained.

'Never mind Roy, you've tried and for that I'm grateful. It seems we'll never solve the mystery of why my mother kept this certificate in her possession, perhaps she never wanted us to know anyway.'

So Rosa abandoned her quest and simply put all thoughts of it to the back of her mind. There were definitely more exciting things to look forward to in the future, as opposed to be looking back at the past.

But in Hull, both Kath and Clive were reluctant to give up on their mission to discover what had happened to his grandmother.

'We can't stop now, not after all the painstaking work we've put in,' Clive announced after mulling it over for several weeks. We've started ...so we'll finish, as they say, but where do we go from here?'

Kath tried to be encouraging, 'I've been told about a website where you can place individual names of a relative on a family tree and then if other people have anyone of the same name on their tree, it will come up with a match. Should I pay to join it?'

'I guess it's worth a try,' Clive agreed, 'but I'm not hopeful.'

That very evening, Kath logged on and subscribed to the site. Excitedly she typed in every relevant name for Clive's grandmother: Margaret Burns - Margaret Purvis - Margaret Fenwick - but all resulted in the same message: No match found.

Clive then suggested, as a last resort, to try the name of Margaret's mother, Mary Patterson.

And this time there was a match!

It was Jim Patterson, a distant relative but sadly he knew nothing of Margaret. However, he gave them a name – the name of a Mr John Keers, living in St Agnes, Cornwall whom he said had a link with Margaret Burns and then he provided the contact details.

Eager to find out more, Kath and Clive sent Mr Keers a short email, asking what he knew of Margaret Burns.

The following morning, Kath turned on the laptop in eager anticipation.

'Clive! Clive! Come and see this, we've had a reply from John's wife, Marion,' she shouted to her husband.

In unison, they read the email, both focussing on the second paragraph...

This is quite strange! This is the second time, in recent months, that we've been contacted by someone looking for a 'Margaret Burns' born in Whitehaven. A family history researcher from Manchester was also searching for her, on behalf of an elderly lady called Rosa, who said her mother Mary Cannon, originally came from Durham and had some connection with Margaret. We don't know anything about Margaret but maybe Rosa could help you, would you like the contact details of the family researcher?

'Look Kath,' Clive said with great optimism, 'both Whitehaven and Durham are mentioned. Could Rosa's mother have a link to my grandmother?'

'Is there even a remote possibility that they could be the same person?' Kath replied. 'We must get in touch with the researcher, you never know we might just be on to finding that final missing piece of the jigsaw.'

Manchester - May 14 2005

At home in Manchester, Rosa was very preoccupied. She was quite concerned about her husband Jack, as his health was not too good and they hadn't been able to get out together in recent months.

It was a normal Saturday morning, when the phone rang.

'I won't be long Jack,' I guess it will be Caroline just checking up on us as usual,' Rosa said as she left her husband's bedside to go answer it.

Half an hour passed before she returned, desperate to tell Jack the cause of her delay. She took a deep intake of breath, before she could begin to speak,

'You're not going to believe what I have to tell you, Jack.'

'What's our Caroline been up to now?' he questioned rather facetiously.

'No, Jack it wasn't our Caroline. It was somebody I didn't know... somebody from Hull. Clive, I think his name was, but he believes that he could be related to me. In fact he thinks that his mother and me were half-sisters!'

'What! What do you mean sisters? You've never had a sister?' Jack interrupted.

Rosa, anxious to continue, just ignored him,

'He then said, I probably also had five half-brothers, although only one is still alive! And what's more he thinks my mother hadn't just been married to Arthur but that she'd had two previous husbands!'

'Well, you didn't believe what he told you, did you lass?' Jack said, shaking his head.

The truth was, at that moment Rosa didn't know what to think or believe. She couldn't take it all in. A man telling her that his grandmother was named Margaret Burns and that he actually thought she'd moved from Durham to Manchester and become Mary Cannon was an almost unbelievable revelation.

'It's strange, Jack,' Rosa continued, as little details of the conversation kept coming back to her,' but he wanted to know if we had a birth certificate with the name Margaret Burns in our possession and of course I had to tell him that we did. Clive told me that he possesses exactly the same certificate for his grandmother, with the same name, date and place of birth on it! That's why he's so sure we're talking about the same person.'

'This is sounding stranger by the minute,' Jack responded, 'but I'm still not convinced that Margaret Burns was your mother, maybe they were just friends.'

'Do you know Jack, I'm going to ring Caroline to see what she thinks about it all.'

'I'll see you in an hour or two's time then,' Jack replied knowingly, smiling at his wife, whom he loved so much.

A week later, a small parcel arrived in the post at Rosa's Manchester home. It was from Clive and contained the one and only photo he had of his grandmother, in her nurse's uniform, plus a picture of himself and his wife Kath and a covering note.

Rosa opened it with some trepidation. When she examined the contents, she was stunned. Studying the picture of Clive's grandmother, she saw a younger version of her own mother looking back at her. Clive's assumption must have been correct, Margaret Burns had to be the same person as Mary Cannon.

'Doesn't Clive look so much like our Tom, too,' Rosa remarked as she shared the pictures with her husband, 'and he's got the look of my mother. The resemblance is uncanny.'

'Especially with the auburn hair!' laughed Jack.

'I must ring Clive and tell him, in fact I'll do it now,' and with that Rosa picked up the phone...

An hour later, Clive put the phone down. A mixture of emotions raged in his head. The search for his missing grandmother appeared to be over but he was shocked by what he'd just been told. He'd thought there could be no more to learn about her but there was and it was even more shocking!

178

'I'm going to have come to terms with the fact that my grandmother was a bigamist,' was the first thought he relayed to his wife.

'I hope it doesn't run in families!' Kath replied, before adding reassuringly, 'I think bigamy was quite common in those days, especially for women eager to achieve a better life, as divorce was not really an option.'

Clive agreed, 'I think you're right, after leaving Allan, it seems my grandmother found real happiness being married to Arthur. Apparently, according to Rosa, she was a wonderful wife and a loving, caring mother.'

'What irony!' Kath replied, 'I don't believe her other children thought that!'

'As for me, I just don't know what to think,' Clive admitted. 'I thought it was dreadful that she abandoned my mother but now to discover the deceit she carried all those years, saying she was called Mary and telling Arthur she was single. Just how did she pull it off?'

'Yes, I guess she must have spent her life looking over her shoulder, almost dreading every knock on the door.'

'Maybe, but I think back then you could get away with it, you certainly wouldn't now.'

Kath smiled, 'This story really is better than all those celebrities on the TV genealogy shows… Surely Margaret must have wondered, a few times, who she actually was!'

Kath paused; there was something she was eager to find out.

'Did Rosa tell you if her mother ever mentioned any family back in Durham because I'm sure she must have thought of them?'

'Apparently, Margaret had always told them that she came from Spennymoor in Durham and that her father was a coal hewer, who'd been killed down the mine but little else. Rosa had absolutely no idea of her mother's secret past.'

'So what you had to reveal must have been very hard for Rosa to take in,' Kath remarked sympathetically, 'I hope she's forgiven us.'

'Well she's eager to meet up… so I guess she has,' Clive reassured her.

It was in late February 2006, when Clive and Kath found their way to Sandbach, in Cheshire, following an invitation to Caroline's house. Meeting Rosa and Jack for the first time was very emotional and both sides felt an immediate connection. The day passed quickly as stories were shared and they exchanged their views on the pathos of Margaret's life.

Rosa was convinced that her mother only acted as she did, simply in order to survive and because she had an absolute dread of the workhouse.

Clive and Kath were reassured to learn that his grandmother had been a genuine, caring person, even though Rosa understood that they might have been tempted to think otherwise.

They also compared photographs and marvelled at the family likeness.

'I think we must be from the same stock,' Clive joked, 'but Kath is hoping I don't have my grandmother's traits!'

Next, Rosa brought out the biscuit tin, 'Here it is, this is what started it all,' she said laughing as she showed Kath and Clive the contents.

'Sorry, Clive, no biscuits inside! This is where we found the certificate for your grandmother Margaret Burns, the one that set me thinking.'

'I'm so pleased you did,' Clive remarked, 'otherwise I'd never have solved the mystery of my missing grandmother.'

'I'm delighted, too,' Rosa added, 'you won't know this, but you solved another long standing puzzle.'

Kath and Clive stared hard at her.

'Please tell us more.'

'It was an event that happened almost sixty years ago and yet I've never forgotten it. Mother was so distraught at the time and yet I could never understand why. But now you've solved it.'

Rosa paused, her voice wavering with emotion.

'You see, if my mother had adopted this false identity, there's no wonder that two men turned up at her house after the census in 1951. And, after checking their records, told her she was 'The Woman Who Didn't Exist'.

Now, at last, I know why!'

EPILOGUE
2014

Rosa is the only surviving member of Margaret's nine children. She now lives alone, after the death of her husband Jack but they did reach their diamond wedding anniversary in 2007. Rosa's elder brother Thomas, died in 2009, aged eighty-five.

Ann, Clive's mother, passed away in 2001, in a nursing home, aged ninety-one. She died, totally unaware of her mother's life in Manchester and always believed that she'd been orphaned as a young child.

Jacob, Margaret's oldest child, finally found a degree of happiness with his second wife Alice, although his life was always marred by his dreadful past. In 1981, he moved with her to Bridlington. Sadly, his sister Ann, lived just twenty miles away but their paths never crossed. In 1991, Jacob moved to Ireland, where he died in Kilbeggan, in 1996, aged eighty-eight.

Ron (Roland), ended his days in Garforth, near Leeds where he'd lived with his wife Anne, having enjoyed fifty-five years of married life. Prior to his death in 2007, aged ninety-four, Clive and Kath shared their findings regarding his mother. Ron accepted it and was pleased to think his mother had found happiness.

John (John-George) spent his married life living in Bristol with his wife Mary. He died in 2003, aged eighty-eight, just six months before their diamond wedding anniversary.

Ivan became a miner after the Second World War and lived in Penshaw, Tyne & Wear, with his wife Jean and two children. He died in 1980, aged sixty, having never met his mother.

John-George Purvis, Margaret's first husband, has no grave because his body was never found. But his name is carved on the Arras Memorial in the Faubourg-D'Amiens Cemetery, which is in the Boulevard du General de Gaulle in the western part of Arras. His brother Henry, is commemorated on the Thiepval Memorial in

Picardy, France.

Their sacrifice for King and Country, giving up their own lives that others might live in freedom, will never be forgotten.

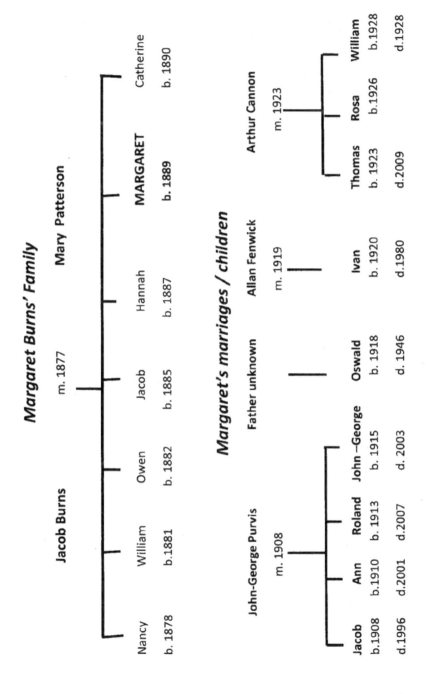

Margaret Burns' Family

Jacob Burns   m. 1877   Mary Patterson

- Nancy b. 1878
- William b.1881
- Owen b. 1882
- Jacob b. 1885
- Hannah b. 1887
- **MARGARET** b. 1889
- Catherine b. 1890

Margaret's marriages / children

John-George Purvis — m. 1908
- Jacob b.1908 d. 1996
- Ann b.1910 d.2001
- Roland b. 1913 d.2007
- John—George b. 1915 d. 2003

Father unknown
- Oswald b. 1918 d. 1946

Allan Fenwick — m. 1919
- Ivan b. 1920 d.1980

Arthur Cannon — m. 1923
- Thomas b. 1923 d.2009
- Rosa b.1926 d.1928
- William b.1928 d.1928

PHOTOGRAPHS

1   Margaret's father, Jacob Burns
2   Jacob Burns and his second wife Marian
3   Allan Fenwick, Margaret's second husband
4   Arthur Herbert Cannon, Margaret's third husband
5   Margaret Purvis (left) outside Prestwich Mental Hospital
6   Jacob Burns, Margaret's first child (middle)
7   Ann Purvis, Margaret's second child
8   Ron Purvis, Margaret's third child
9   John Purvis, Margaret's fourth child
10   Ivan Fenwick, Margaret's sixth child
11   Thomas Cannon, Margaret's seventh child
12   Rosa Cannon, Margaret's eighth child, aged 16
13   Margaret Cannon, pictured in 1944
14   Kath and Clive Richardson

BIBLIOGRAPHY

Ordinary Lives - A hundred years ago - Carol Adams
1914-1918 - Stephanie Audoin-Rouzeau & Annette Becker
Tommy goes to War - Malcolm Brown
Life in Edwardian England - Robert Cecil
Born 1900, a human history - Hunter Davies
Durham Men in the Great War - John Davison
The Quick and the Dead - Richard van Emden
Veterans - the last survivors of the Great War - Richard van Emden &Steve Humphries
How our ancestors lived - David Hey
For King and Country - Brian MacArthur
The Durham Forces in the Fields - Captain Wilfrid Miles
Memories of Pelton - Dorothy Rand & George Nairn
The Great Silence, 1918-1920 - Juliet Nicholson
No Finer Courage - Michael Senior
Memories of Crumpsall - Barbara Shaw
The Raising of Kitchener's Army - Peter Simpkins
Life on all fronts - Women in WW1 - Gill Thomas
The Bowburn Local History Society Archives

12

13